In the confined space of the compartment the alien's distress call was deafening.

Conway cursed his own stupidity as the panic-stricken Gogleskan stumbled about the floor within a few feet of him.

The FOKT's dumpy body lurched past. Its multicolored hair was erect and twitching, its four stings were fully extended. Droplets of venom oozed from the tips. Conway lay rigid as the being moved away and then approached again.

From the corner of his eye Conway saw the Gogleskan stop, one of its stings only inches away from his face, the bristles of its hair touching his coveralls. Its breath puffed gently across his forehead.

If he moved, he knew with a dreadful certainty that the Gogleskan would sting him . . .

Also from Orbit by James White:

MAJOR OPERATION
STAR SURGEON
AMBULANCE SHIP
HOSPITAL STATION
ALL JUDGEMENT FLED
SECTOR GENERAL

JAMES WHITE

Star Healer

A *Sector General* Novel

Futura

An Orbit Book

First published in 1985 in the USA by Ballantine Books

First published in Great Britain in 1987
by Futura Publications, a Division of
Macdonald & Co (Publishers) Ltd
London & Sydney

All characters in this publication are fictitious and any resemblance to real persons, living or dead, is purely coincidental.

ISBN 0 7088 8187 4

Printed and bound in Great Britain by
Cox & Wyman Ltd, Reading

Futura Publications
A Division of
Macdonald & Co (Publishers) Ltd
Greater London House
Hampstead Road
London NW1 7QX
A BPCC plc Company

Chapter 1

SOMETHING struck Conway as odd about the latest bunch of trainees as he stood aside to allow them to precede him into the observation gallery of the Hudlar Children's Ward. It was not that among the fourteen of them they comprised five widely different life-forms or that their treatment of him—he was, after all, a Senior Physician attached to the galaxy's largest multienvironment hospital—was condescending to the point of rudeness.

To be accepted for advanced training at Sector Twelve General Hospital a candidate—in addition to possessing a high degree of medical and surgical ability—had to be able to adapt to and accept people and circumstances which, back in their home-planet hospitals, they could barely have imagined. At home an off-planet patient would be a rarity indeed, while at Sector General they would be treating nothing else. Furthermore, many of them would find it difficult to make the transition from highly respected member of the local medical fraternity to mere trainee at Sector General, but they would soon settle in.

His mind was playing tricks on him, Conway decided—probably because he had so much on it at the present time. A rumor was going around about changes in his ambulance ship setup, and he was scheduled for an hour early that afternoon with the Chief Psychologist, always an unsettling prospect.

Conway was also irritated because he seemed to be coming in for more than his fair share of short-term projects and medical odd jobs—such as giving the trainees their initial orientation tour. His special ambulance-ship team had had very few calls in recent months.

"The patients in the ward below are infant Hudlars," Conway explained when the trainees had formed an untidy crescent around and behind him. "They belong to an immensely strong species and, as adults, are extremely resistant to physical injury and disease. So much so that the concept of curative medical treatment has been foreign to them. No medical profession exists on Hudlar, and the high infant mortality rate of the recent past was simply accepted. Their young fall prey to a large number of indigenous pathogens from the moment they are born, and those which do not quickly develop or inherit resistance to them perish. The hospital is trying to develop a wide-spectrum immunization procedure to be carried out during the prenatal stage, but so far with limited success."

He indicated a young Hudlar standing just below them, looking up. "You will already have deduced from this individual's general stance and musculature that the species evolved on a world with very heavy gravity and proportionately high atmospheric pressure, both of which have been reproduced in the ward. You will also observe no beds or rest furniture; patients who can move simply roam about at will. This is because their body tegument is so tough that padded rest areas are unnecessary. Because of the difficulty other species have in telling Hudlars apart, patient ID and case history are impressed magnetically on the metal band attached to the left forelimb. The Hudlars' six limbs can serve as either manipulatory or locomotor appendages.

"While gravity and atmospheric pressure have been duplicated here," Conway went on, "the exact constituents of their atmosphere have not been reproduced. Their home world's air is a thick, semiliquid soup laden with tiny, airborne food particles which are absorbed and excreted by specialized areas of the skin. We find it more convenient to spray them periodically with a nutrient paint, as two of the armored medical attendants are doing now.

"With the facts now in your possession," he said, turning to regard them, "would anyone like to classify this life-form?"

For a moment there was no verbal response. The Orligian DBDGs moved restively, but the expressions on their humanoid features were concealed by facial hair. The silvery fur of the caterpillarlike Kelgian DBLFs was in constant motion, but the emotions which the movements expressed were readable only by a fellow member of the species or by a being carrying a Kelgian tape in its mind. As for the elephantine Tralthan FGLIs and the diminutive Dewatti EGCLs, their features were too decentralized to be visible in their entirety, while the hard, angular mandibles and deeply recessed eyes of the Melfan ELNTs were completely expressionless.

One of the four Melfan trainees first broke the silence. Its translator hummed briefly, "They belong to physiological classification FROB."

It was difficult to tell Melfans apart at the best of times, since all adult ELNTs possessed similar body mass and the only visible differences were the subtle variations in marking on the upper carapace. To make identification even more difficult, two of the four Melfan trainees seemed to be identical twins. One of these had spoken.

"Correct," Conway said approvingly. "Your name, Doctor?"

"Danalta, Senior Physician."

Polite, too, Conway thought. "Very well, Danalta. But you were slow in making the identification even though your colleagues were even slower. All of you must learn to quickly and accurately classify—"

"With respect, Senior Physician," the Melfan broke in, "I did not wish to offer gratuitous display of my medical knowledge, woefully limited as it is at present, until my colleagues had a chance to respond. I have studied all that was available to me regarding your physiological classification system. But I come from a backward world where the level of technology is low and intercultural communication has been limited, particularly where medical data on this hospital was concerned.

"Besides," it concluded, "the Hudlar life-form is distinctive, unique, and could only be FROB."

Conway would not have described Melf as a backward world and neither would any other member of the Galactic Federation, so this Danalta must have come from one of the colonies recently seeded by Melf. To qualify for Sector General with a background like that required determination as well as professional competence. It did not matter that the Melfan was turning out to be an odd combination of polite, self-effacing smart aleck—the operative word was "smart," and the best assistants an overworked Senior could have were those who strived to render their superiors redundant. He decided that he would keep a close watch on Danalta's progress, for purely selfish reasons.

"Since it is possible," Conway said drily, "that a number of your colleagues are less well-informed on this subject than you, I shall outline very briefly the system of life-form identification which we use here. Your various specialist tutors will take you through it in more detail."

He looked for Danalta, but the trainees had changed their positions and Conway could no longer tell which of the two identical Melfans was which. He went on, "Unless you have already been attached to a multienvironment hospital, you will normally have encountered off-world patients one species at a time, probably on a short-term basis as the result of a ship accident or some emergency, and you would refer to them by their planets of origin. But here—where rapid and accurate identification of incoming patients is vital because all too often they are in no condition to furnish physiological data themselves—we have evolved a four-letter physiological classification system. It works like this.

"The first letter denotes the level of physical evolution reached by the species when it acquired intelligence," he continued. "The second indicates the type and distribution of limbs, sense organs, and body orifices, and the remaining two letters refer to the combination of metabolism and food and air requirements associated with the home planet's gravity and atmospheric pressure, which in turn gives an indication of the physical mass and protective tegument possessed by the being."

Conway smiled, although he knew that a long time would elapse before any of the trainees would be able to recognize that peculiarly Earth-human facial grimace for what it was. "Usually I have to remind some of our extraterrestrial candidates at this point that the initial letter of their classification should not be allowed to give them feelings of inferiority, because the degree of physical evolution is controlled by environmental factors and bears little relation to the level of intelligence..."

Species with the prefix A, B, or C, he went on to explain, were water-breathers. On most worlds life had originated in the sea, and these beings had developed intelligence without having to leave it. D through F were warm-blooded oxygen-breathers, into which group most of the intelligent races of the Federation fell, and the G and K types were also oxygen breathing, but insectile. The Ls and Ms were light-gravity, winged beings.

Chlorine-breathing life-forms were contained in the O and P groups, and after these came the more exotic, the more highly evolved physically and the downright weird types. Into these categories fell the radiation-eaters, the cold-blooded or crystalline beings, and entities capable of modifying their physical structures at will. However, those beings possessing extrasensory powers sufficiently well developed to make ambulatory or manipulatory appendages unnecessary were given the prefix V regardless of their size or shape.

"There are anomalies in the system," Conway went on, "and these must be blamed on a lack of imagination and foresight by the originators. The AACP life-form, for instance, has a vegetable metabolism. Normally the A prefix denotes a water-breather, there being nothing lower on the evolutionary scale than the piscatorial life-forms, but the AACPs are intelligent vegetables and plant-life came before the fish."

Conway pointed suddenly at a nurse who was spraying nutrient onto a young Hudlar at the other end of the ward, then turned toward Danalta. "Perhaps you would like to classify that life-form, Doctor."

"I am not Danalta," the Melfan Conway was addressing protested. Even though the process of translation tended to filter the emotional overtones from messages, the ELNT sounded displeased.

"My apologies," Conway said, looking around for its twin, in vain. He decided that Danalta, for reasons known only to itself, had hidden behind the group of Tralthan trainees. Before he could redirect the question, one of the Tralthans answered it.

"The being you indicate is encased in a heavy-duty protective suit," the big FGLI said, this deep modulated rumblings of its native speech reinforcing the ponderous and pedantic style of the translated words. "The only part of the being visible to me is the small area behind the visor, and this is indistinct because of reflections from the ward lighting. Since the protective suit is self-propelled, there is no evidence available as to the number and type of the locomotor appendages. But the overall size and shape of the suit together with the positioning of the four mechanical manipulators spaced around the base of the conical head section—assuming that for ergonomic reasons these mechanical extensions approximate the positions of the underlying natural limbs—leads me to state with a fair degree of certainty that the entity in question is a Kelgian of physiological classification DBLF. Glimpses of a gray, furry tegument and what appears to be one of the Kelgian visual sensors revealed, however unclearly, through the small area of the visor, supports this identification."

"Very *good*, Doctor!" But before Conway could ask the Tralthan its name, the entrance lock of the ward swung open and a large, spherical vehicle mounted on caterpillar treads rolled in. The sphere was encircled equatorially by a variety of remote handling and sensory devices, and prominently displayed on the forward upper surface was the insignia of a Diagnostician. Instead, Conway pointed to the vehicle and said, "Can you classify that one?"

This time one of the Kelgians spoke first.

"Only by inference and deduction, Senior Physician,"

it said as slow, regular waves rippled along its fur from nose to tail. "Plainly the vehicle is a self-powered pressure vessel which, judging by the external bracing evident on the sphere, is designed to protect the ward patients and medical staff as well as the occupant. The walking limbs, if there are any, are concealed by the pressure envelope, and I would say that the number of external handling and sensory devices is so large that it is probable the being has only a small number of natural manipulators and sensors, and operates the external devices as required. The walls of the pressure vessel are of unknown thickness, so that there is no accurate data available to me regarding the size and physical configuration of the occupant."

The Kelgian paused for a moment and sat back on its rearmost legs, looking like a fat, furry question mark. Silvery ripples continued to move slowly along its back and flanks, while the fur of its three fellow DBLFs twitched and tufted and flattened randomly as if there were a strong wind blowing in the observation gallery.

An air of restlessness, of low-key agitation, seemed to pervade the other members of the group. The Tralthans were each raising and lowering their stumpy, elephantine feet in turn. The continuous clicking and scraping sound was the Melfans tapping their crablike legs against the floor, while the teeth of the Orligians showed whitely in their dark, furry faces. Conway hoped they were smiling.

"I am aware of two life-forms which use a pressure vessel of this kind," the Kelgian went on. "They are utterly dissimilar in environmental requirements and physiology, and both would be considered by the more common oxygen- and chlorine-breathing species to be among the exotic categories. One is a frigid-blooded methane-breather who is most comfortable in an environment at a few degrees above absolute zero, and who evolved on the perpetually dark worlds which have been detached from their original solar systems and drift through the interstellar spaces.

"Physically they are quite small," the Kelgian continued, "averaging one-third of the body mass of a being like myself. But during contact with other species, the highly refrigerated life-support and sensory translation systems which they are forced to wear are large and complex and require frequent power recharge..."

Three of them! Conway thought. He looked around for the Tralthan who had correctly tagged the suited DBLF, and Danalta, the Melfan trainee who had identified the FROB, to observe their reactions to the very knowledgeable Kelgian—but the group was milling about so much that he could not tell who was who. Certainly he had sensed something unusual about this bunch shortly after taking charge of them at the hospital's staff entry port.

"...The other life-form," the Kelgian was saying, "inhabits a heavy-gravity, watery planet which circles very close to its parent sun. It breathes superheated steam and has a quite interesting metabolism about which I am incompletely informed. It, also, is a small life-form, and the large size of its pressure envelope is necessitated by its having to mount heaters to render the occupant comfortable, and surface insulation and refrigerators to keep the vicinity habitable by other life-forms.

"The environment of the Hudlar ward is warm with a high moisture content," the Kelgian continued, "and some measure of the low internal temperature required by a methane-breathing SNLU would be conducted, no matter how efficient the insulation, to the outer fabric of the vehicle, where condensation would be apparent. Since condensation is not present, the probability is high that the vehicle contains the high-temperature life-form, a member of which species is said to be a Diagnostician at the hospital.

"This identification is the result of deduction, guesswork, and a degree of prior knowledge, Senior Physician," the Kelgian ended, "but I would place the entity in physiological classification TLTU."

Conway looked closely at the slow, regular fur movements of the unusually unemotional and well-informed DBLF, and then at the agitated pelts of its Kelgian colleagues. Speaking slowly, because his mind was moving at top speed and little of it was free for speech, he said, "The answer is correct, no matter how you arrived at it."

He was thinking about the DBLF classification, and in particular about their expressive fur. Because of inadequacies in the speech organs, the Kelgian spoken language lacked emotional expression. Instead the beings' highly mobile fur acted, so far as another Kelgian was concerned, as a perfect but uncontrollable mirror to the speaker's emotional state. As a result the concept of lying was totally alien to them, and the idea of being tactful or diplomatic or even polite was utterly unthinkable. A DBLF invariably said exactly what it meant, and felt, because its fur revealed its feelings from moment to moment and to do otherwise would be sheer stupidity.

Conway was also thinking about the Melfan ELNTs and their mechanism of reproduction which made twinning an impossibility, and about the phrasing of the answers volunteered by Danalta and the other two, particularly that of the Kelgian who had implied that the TLTU life-form was not particularly exotic. From the moment they had arrived, he had felt that something was distinctly unusual about the group. He should have trusted his feelings.

He thought back to his first sight of the newcomers and of how they had looked and acted at different times since then, especially their nervousness and the general lack of questioning about the hospital. Was some kind of conspiracy afoot? Without being obtrusive about it, he looked at each of them.

Four Kelgian DBLFs, two Dewatti EGCLs, three Tralthan FGLIs, three Melfan ELNTs, and two Orligian DBDGs—fourteen in all. *But Kelgians are never polite or respectful or capable of much control over their fur*, Conway thought as he deliberately turned away from them and looked into the ward.

"Who's the joker?" he said.

No one replied, and Conway, still without looking at them, said, "I have no previous knowledge of the life-form concerned, and my identification is based, therefore, on inference, deduction, and behavioral observation..."

The sarcasm in his voice was probably lost in the translation, and the majority of extraterrestrials were literal-minded to a fault, anyway. He softened his tone as he went on. "I am addressing that entity among you whose species is amoebic in that it can extrude any limbs, sense organs, or protective tegument necessary to the environment or situation in which it finds itself. My guess is that it evolved on a planet with a highly eccentric orbit, and with climatic changes so severe that an incredible degree of physical adaptability was necessary for survival. It became dominant on its world, developed intelligence and a civilization, not by competing in the matter of natural weapons but by refining and perfecting the adaptive capability. When it was faced by natural enemies, the options would be flight, protective mimicry, or the assumption of a shape frightening to the attacker.

"The speed and accuracy of the mimicry displayed here," he continued, "particularly in the almost perfect reproduction of behavior patterns, suggests that the entity may be a receptive empath. With such effective means of self-protection available, I would say that the species is impervious to physical damage other than by physical annihilation or the application of ultrahigh temperatures, so that the concept of curative surgery would be a strange one indeed to members of that race. Virtual physical indestructability would mean that they did not require mechanisms for self-protection, so they are likely to be advanced in the philosophical sciences but backward in developing their technology.

"I would identify you," Conway said, swinging around to face them, "as physiological classification TOBS."

He walked rapidly toward the three Orligians, for the good reason that there should have been only two of them. Quickly but gently he reached out to their shoulders and slipped a finger between the straps of their harnesses and the underlying fur. On the third attempt he could not do it because the harness and the fur would not separate.

Drily, Conway said, "Do you have any future plans or ambitions, Doctor Danalta, other than playing practical jokes?"

For a moment the head and shoulders melted and slumped into what could have been the beginnings of a

Melfan carapace—the sort of disquieting metamorphosis, Conway thought, which he would have to get used to—before it firmed back to the Orligian shape.

"I am most sincerely sorry, Senior Physician," Danalta said, "if my recent actions have caused you mental distress. The matter of physical shape is normally of complete indifference to me, but I thought that adopting the forms of the people within the hospital would be more convenient for purposes of communication and social intercourse, and I also wished to practice my mimicry as soon and as often as possible before a being who was most likely to spot any inconsistencies. On the ferrycraft I discussed it with the other members of the group, and they agreed to cooperate.

"My chief purpose in seeking a position at the hospital," Danalta went on quickly, "was to have the opportunity of working with so large and varied a group of life-forms. To a mimic of my capabilities—and at this point I should say that they are considered greater than average among my people—this establishment represents a tremendous challenge, even though I fully realize that there will be life-forms which I may not be able to reproduce. Regarding the word 'joker,' this does not seem to translate into my language. But if I have given offense in this matter, I apologize without reservation."

"Your apology is accepted," Conway said, thinking of some of the harebrained stunts his own group of trainees had been up to many years ago—activities which had only the most tenuous connection with the practice of medicine. He looked at his watch and added, "If you are interested in meeting a large number of different life-forms, Doctor, you will shortly have your wish. All of you, please follow me."

But the Orligian who was not an Orligian did not move. It said, "As you rightly deduced, Senior Physician, the practice of medicine is completely foreign to our species. My purpose in coming here is selfish, even pleasurable, rather than idealistic. I shall merely be using my abilities to reassure beings who are suffering from physical malfunctions by mimicking them if there are no members of their own race present to give such reassurance. Or to adapt quickly to environments which others would find lethal so that urgent treatment would not be delayed because of time wasted in the donning of protective envelopes. Or to extrude limbs of a specialized shape or function which might be capable of repairing otherwise inaccessible areas where an organic malfunction had occurred. But I am not, and should not be called, a doctor."

Conway laughed suddenly. He said, "If that is the kind of work you plan to do here, Danalta, we won't call you anything else."

Chapter 2

LIKE a gigantic, cylindrical Christmas tree Sector Twelve General Hospital hung in the interstellar darkness between the rim of the parent Galaxy and the densely populated star systems of the Greater Magellanic Cloud. In its three hundred and eighty-four levels were reproduced the environments of all the intelligent life-forms known to the Galactic Federation, a biological spectrum ranging from the ultrafrigid methane life-forms through the more common oxygen-breathing types up to the weird and wonderful beings who did not breathe, or even eat, but existed by the direct absorption of hard radiation.

Sector General represented a two-fold miracle of engineering and psychology. Its supply and maintenance were handled by the Monitor Corps—the Federation's executive and law-enforcement arm—which also saw to its nonmedical administration. But the traditional friction between military and civilian members of the staff did not occur, and neither were there any serious problems among its ten thousand-odd medical personnel, who were composed of nearly seventy differing life-forms with as many different mannerisms, body odors, and ways of looking at life.

But space was always at a premium in Sector General, and whenever possible the beings who worked together were expected to eat together—though not, of course, of the same food.

The trainees were lucky enough to find two adjoining tables, unlucky in that the furniture and eating utensils were designed for the use of dwarflike Nidian DBDGs. The vast dining hall catered to the warm-blooded, oxygen-breathing members of the staff, and one look around made plain that different species dined or talked shop or simply gossiped together at the same table. Wrong-size furniture was a discomfort which the newcomers would get used to and, in this instance, things could have been much worse.

The Melfan's mandibles were at the right height above the table, and it was no inconvenience for the ELNTs to eat while standing. The Tralthans did everything including sleeping on their six blocky feet. The Kelgians could adapt their caterpillar shapes to any type of furniture, and the Orligians, like Conway himself, could sit without too much discomfort on the armrests of the chairs. The tiny Dewatti had no problems at all, and the polymorphic Danalta had taken the shape of a Dewatti.

"The food-ordering and delivery system is standard," Conway said, looking from one table to the other, "and the same as that used on the ships which brought you here. If you punch in your physiological classification, the menu will be displayed in your own written language. Except for Danalta. There are no special dietary requirements for the TOBS life-form, I suspect, but no doubt you have preferences? Danalta!..."

"Your pardon, Senior Physician," the TOBS said. While it watched the dining hall entrance, its body was twisted into a shape impossible for a Dewatti. "My attention was taken by the incredible assortment of beings who come and go here."

"What would you like to eat?" Conway asked patiently.

The TOBS spoke without turning its Dewatti head. "Virtually anything which is not radioactive or chemically corrosive, Senior Physician. Were nothing else available I could, in a short time, metabolize the material of this dining furniture. But I eat infrequently and will not need to do so again for several of your days."

"Fine." Conway tapped for a steak before going on. "And Danalta, while it is very pleasant, and rare in this establishment, to be addressed properly and with respect, it can be cumbersome. So it is customary to address interns, Junior and Senior Physicians, and even Diagnosticians as Doctor. Have you seen a physiological type which you cannot reproduce?"

Conway was beginning to feel irritated at the way Danalta kept looking at the entrance while he was speaking, and wondered if it was a trait peculiar to the species and the impoliteness unintentional. Then he nearly choked when he saw that the TOBS had extruded a small eye from the back of its head to watch him.

"I have certain limitations, Doctor," it replied. "Shape changing is relatively easy, but I cannot discard physical mass. This . . ."—it indicated itself—"is a small but very heavy Dewatti. And the entity who has just entered would be very difficult to reproduce."

Conway followed the direction of its other eyes, then stood up suddenly and waved.

"Prilicla!"

The little being who had just entered the dining hall was a Cinrusskin GLNO—a six-legged, exoskeletal, multi-winged, incredibly fragile insect. The gravity of its home world was one-twelfth Earth normal, and only double sets of gravity nullifiers kept it from being smashed flat against the floor, enabled it to fly or, when the unthinking movements of its more massive colleagues threatened life and ultrafragile limb, to scamper safely along the walls or ceiling. It was impossible for off-worlders to tell Cinrusskins apart; even Cinrusskins could only differentiate between members of the species by the identification of individual emotional radiation. But there was only one

GLNO empath on the hospital staff; this one had to be Senior Physician Prilicla.

The occupants of both tables were watching the little empath as it flew slowly toward them on its wide, iridescent, almost transparent wings. As it came to a gentle halt above them, Conway noticed a faint, erratic trembling in the six pipe-stem legs and its hover showed definite signs of instability.

Something was distressing the little Cinrusskin, but Conway did not say anything, because he knew that his own concern was already obvious to the empath. He wondered suddenly if the sight of the GLNO had triggered some deep-seated phobia in one of the new arrivals and it was radiating fear or revulsion with sufficient intensity to affect Prilicla's coordination.

He would have to put a stop to *that*.

"This is Senior Physician Prilicla," he said quickly, as if we was making a simple introduction. "It is a native of Cinruss, a GLNO, and possesses a highly developed empathic faculty which, among other uses, is invaluable in detecting and monitoring the condition of deeply unconscious patients. The faculty also makes it highly sensitive to the emotional radiation of colleagues such as ourselves who are conscious. In Prilicla's presence we must guard against sudden and violent mental reactions, even involuntary reactions such as instinctive fear or dislike at meeting a life-form which, on another species' home planet, is a predator or the object of a childhood phobia. These feelings and reactions must be controlled and negated to the best of your abilities because they will be experienced with greater intensity by the empath. When you become better acquainted with Prilicla, you will find that it is impossible to have unpleasant feelings toward it.

"And I apologize, Prilicla, for making you the subject of that impromptu lecture without first asking your permission."

"No need, friend Conway. I am aware of your feeling of concern, which was the reason for giving the lecture, and I thank you for it. But no unpleasant feelings exist among this group. Their emotional radiation is composed of surprise, incredulity, and intense curiosity, which I will be pleased to satisfy—"

"But you're still shaking..." Conway began quietly. Uncharacteristically the Cinrusskin ignored him.

"...I am also aware of another empath," it went on, drifting along between the tables until it hovered above the psuedo-Dewatti with the extra eye. "You must be the newly arrived polymorph life-form from Fotawn. I look forward to working with you, friend Danalta. This is my first encounter with the extremely gifted TOBS classification."

"And I with a GLNO, Doctor Prilicla," Danalta replied as its Dewatti shape slumped and began to overflow the chair in what had to be a pleased reaction at such words from a Senior Physician. "But my empathic faculty is not nearly as sensitive and well developed as yours. It evolved with the shape-changing ability as an early warning of the intentions of nearby predators. Unlike the faculty possessed by your race, which is used as the primary system of nonverbal communication, mine is under voluntary control so that the level of emotional radiation reaching my receptors can be reduced or even cut off at will should it become too distressing."

Prilicla agreed that a shutoff was a useful option, and ignoring Conway, they turned to discussing their home-world environments, the gentle, light-gravity world of Cinruss and Fotawn, the utterly frightful and inimicable planet of the TOBS. The others, to whom Cinruss and Fotawn were little more than names, listened with great interest, only occasionally breaking in with questions.

Conway, who could be as patient as anyone when all other options were closed to him, concentrated on finishing his meal before the downwash from Prilicla's wings cooled it into inedibility.

He was not surprised that the two empaths were getting on well together—that was a law of nature. An emotion-sensitive who by word, deed, or omission caused hostility in the people around it had those same feelings bounced back in its face, so it was in an empath's own interest to make the atmosphere as pleasant as possible for all concerned. Danalta, apparently, was somewhat different in that it could switch off incoming emotional radiation at will.

Neither was Conway surprised that the TOBS knew so much about Cinruss and its empathic natives—Danalta had already demonstrated its wide-ranging knowledge about everything and everybody. What did surprise him was that Prilicla seemed to know a lot about Fotawn that had not come up in the present conversation, and Conway had the impression that the knowledge was recently acquired. But from whom?

Certainly it was not common knowledge in the hospital, Conway thought as he kept his eyes on his dessert, with an occasional glance upward to where Prilicla was maintaining its unstable hover. From habit he did not look at the various unsavory, foul-smelling messes which the others were busy ingesting. Had news of Fotawn and its visiting TOBS leaked, the hospital grapevine would have been twitching with it in its every leaf and branch. So why had Prilicla alone been given the information?

"I'm curious," Conway stated during the next lull in the conversation.

"I know." The trembling in Prilicla's limbs increased momentarily. "I am an empath, friend Conway."

"And I," Conway replied, "after the number of years we have worked together, have developed a degree of empathy where you are concerned, little friend. There is a problem."

It was a statement rather than a question, and Prilicla's flying became even more unstable, so that it had to alight on an unoccupied space at the table. When it spoke it seemed to be choosing the words with great care, and Conway reminded himself that the empath was not in the least averse to lying if in so doing it could maintain a pleasant level of emotional radiation in the area.

"I have had a lengthy meeting with friend O'Mara," Prilicla said, "during which I was given some disturbing news."

"Which was?" Conway felt that he should have obtained a degree in extraterrestrial dentistry; on this occasion getting information out of Prilicla was like pulling teeth.

"I am sure that I will adjust to it in time," the empath replied. "Do not be concerned for me. I . . . I have been promoted to a position of much greater responsibility and authority. Please understand, friend Conway, I accepted with reluctance."

"Congratulations!" Conway was delighted. "And there was no need for the reluctance, or for you to feel badly about it. O'Mara would not give you the job unless he was absolutely sure you could do it. What exactly will you be doing?"

"I would rather not discuss it here and now, friend Conway." Prilicla's tremor was increasing as it forced itself to say something which verged on the disagreeable. "This is not the time or the place to talk shop."

Conway choked on his coffee. In this place shop was normally the only subject of conversation, and they both knew it. What was more, the presence of the newcomers should have been no bar, because they would have been interested in listening to a discussion between senior members of staff of matters which they did not quite understand, but which they soon would. He had never known Prilicla to behave like this before, and the intensity of his curiosity was making the empath shake even harder.

"What did O'Mara say to you?" Conway asked firmly, and added, "Exactly."

"He said," Prilicla replied quickly, "that I should assume more responsibility, learn to give orders, and generally throw my weight around. Friend Conway, my physical mass is inconsiderable, my musculature virtually nonexistent, and I feel that the thought processes of the Chief Psychologist are, well, difficult to fathom. But right now I must excuse myself. There are some routine matters to which I must attend on *Rhabwar*, and I had, in any case, planned on having lunch in the ambulance ship."

Conway did not have to be an empath to know that the empath was uncomfortable and did not want to answer any more questions.

A few minutes after Prilicla departed, he handed over the trainees to the instructors who had been waiting patiently for them to finish lunch, and he had a few more minutes in which to think before a trio of Kelgian nurses joined the next table and began moaning and twitching their fur at each other. He switched off his translator so that their conversation, a highly scandalous tale about another member of their species, would not distract him.

Prilicla would not display continuous emotional disturbance simply because it had received news of a promotion. It had borne heavy medical and surgical responsibilities on many previous occasions. Neither would it mind giving orders. True, it had no weight to throw about, but then it always gave its instructions in such a polite and inoffensive way that its subordinates would have died rather than make it feel unhappy by refusing to obey. And the newcomers had not been emoting unpleasantly and neither had Conway.

But suppose Conway *would* have felt badly if Prilicla had told him the details of its new job? That would explain the empath's uncharacteristic behavior, because the thought of hurting another being's feelings would be highly unpleasant for it—especially if the person concerned was a close friend like Conway. And for some reason Prilicla would not, or could not, speak about its new position in front of the newcomers, or perhaps before one of the newcomers.

Maybe it was not its new job which was worrying Prilicla but something it had learned during its meeting with O'Mara, something which concerned Conway himself and which the Cinrusskin was not at liberty to divulge. He checked the time and stood up quickly, excusing himself to the nurses.

The answers—and, he knew from long experience, very likely a whole new set of problems—would be found in the office of the Chief Psychologist.

Chapter 3

THE inner office of the Chief Psychologist resembled in many respects a medieval torture chamber, and the resemblance was heightened not only by the wide variety of extraterrestrial couches and relaxers fitted with physical restraints, but by the graying, granite-featured Torquemada in Monitor Corps green who presided over it. Major O'Mara indicated a physiologically suitable chair.

"Sit down, Doctor," he said with a completely uncharacteristic smile. "Relax. You've been dashing about in that ambulance ship of yours so much recently that I've scarcely seen you. It is high time that we had a good, long talk."

Conway felt his mouth go dry. *This is going to be rough*. But what had he done or left undone to merit this sort of treatment?

The other's features were as unreadable as a lump of rock, but the eyes which were studying him, Conway knew from long experience, opened into a mind so keenly analytical that it gave the Major what amounted to a telepathic faculty. Conway did not speak and neither, for a long moment, did O'Mara.

As Chief Psychologist of the Federation's largest multi-environment hospital, he was responsible for the mental well-being of a huge medical staff belonging to more than sixty different species. Even though his Monitor Corps rank of major—which had been conferred on him for purely administrative reasons—did not place him high in the hospital's chain of command, there were no clear limits to his authority. To O'Mara the medical staff were potential patients, and a large part of the Psychology

Department's work was the assignment of the right kind of doctor to a given patient.

Even with the highest degrees of tolerance and mutual respect, dangerous situations could arise among the staff because of ignorance or misunderstanding, or a being could develop xenophobia—in spite of the strict psychological screening every Sector General candidate had to undergo before being accepted for training—to a degree which threatened to affect its professional competence, mental stability, or both. An Earth-human doctor, for example, who had a strong subconscious fear of spiders would not be able to bring to bear on a Cinrusskin patient the proper degree of clinical detachment necessary for its treatment. And if someone like Prilicla were to treat such an Earth-human patient...

A large part of O'Mara's responsibility was to detect and eradicate such trouble among the medical staff while the other members of his department saw to it that the problems did not arise again—to such an extent that Earth-humans knowledgeable in matters of planetary history referred to the process as the Second Inquisition. According to O'Mara himself, however, the true reason for the high level of mental stability among his charges was that they were all too frightened of him to risk publicly displaying even a minor neurosis.

O'Mara smiled suddenly and said, "I think you are overdoing the respectful silence, Doctor. I would like to talk to you and, contrary to my usual practice, you will be allowed to talk back. Are you happy with ambulance ship duty?"

Normally the Chief Psychologist's manner was caustic, sarcastic, and abrupt to the point of rudeness. He was fond of saying by way of explanation—O'Mara never apologized for anything—that with his colleagues he could relax and be his usual bad-tempered, obnoxious self while with potential patients he had to display sympathy and understanding. Knowing that, Conway did not feel at all reassured by his uncharacteristically pleasant Chief Psychologist.

"Quite happy," Conway said guardedly.

"You weren't happy in the beginning." O'Mara was watching him intently. "As I remember, Doctor, you thought it beneath the dignity of a Senior Physician to be given medical charge of an ambulance ship. Any problems with the ship's officers or the medical team? Any personnel changes you might care to suggest?"

"That was before I realized what a very special ambulance ship *Rhabwar* was," Conway said, answering the questions in order. "There are no problems. The ship runs smoothly, the Monitor Corps crew are efficient and cooperative, and the members of the medical team are... No, I cannot think of any possible change that should be made in the personnel."

"I can." For an instant there was a caustic edge to the Chief Psychologist's tone, as if the O'Mara that Conway knew and did not particularly love was trying to break through. Then he smiled and went on. "Surely you must have considered the disadvantages, the inconvenience and disruption caused by constantly remaining on ambulance ship standby, and you must have felt a degree of irritation that every operation you perform at Sector General requires that a surgical understudy be prepared in case you were to be suddenly called away. And the ambulance ship duty means that you cannot take part in some of the projects which your seniority would warrant. Research, teaching, making your experience available to others instead of dashing all over the Galaxy on rescue missions and—"

"So the change will be me," Conway broke in angrily. "But who will be my?..."

"Prilicla will head *Rhabwar*'s medical team," O'Mara replied, "but it accepted only on condition that in so doing it did not cause its friend Conway serious mental distress. It was quite adamant about that, for a Cinrusskin. Even though I told it not to say anything to you until you had been told officially, I expected it to go straight to you with the news."

"It did. But it only mentioned a promotion, nothing else. I was with a party of new trainees and Prilicla seemed more interested in an empathic polymorph called Danalta.

But I could see that something was troubling our little friend."

"Several things were troubling Prilicla," O'Mara said. "It knew that when you moved from *Rhabwar*, it moved up to your job, and that Danalta had already been chosen to fill its vacancy. But the TOBS doesn't know about this yet, so Prilicla couldn't tell you the details of its new job, because if Danalta learned about its appointment at second hand it might decide that it was being insulted by being taken for granted. The TOBS are a very able species and justifiably proud of their abilities, and its psych profile indicates that it would certainly take umbrage in a situation like that. But the job it is being offered is physiologically challenging to a polymorph, and I expect Danalta to jump at it.

"Have you any serious objections to these changes, Doctor?" he added.

"No." Conway wondered why he did not feel angrier and more disappointed at losing a position which was the envy of his colleagues, and which he himself found exciting and professionally demanding. He added sourly, "If the changes are necessary in the first place."

"They are necessary," O'Mara said seriously, and went on. "I am not in the habit of paying compliments, as you know. My job here is to shrink heads, not swell them. Neither do I discuss my reasons for taking particular actions or decisions. But this is not a routine matter."

The psychologist's square, stubby hands were spread out on the desk before him, and his face was bent forward, looking at them as he spoke,

"First," he said, "you were the medical team leader on *Rhabwar*'s maiden flight. Since then there have been many successful rescue missions, the procedures for the recovery and treatment of survivors have been perfected, and you are leaving a most efficient ambulance ship in which nothing serious can go wrong because of a small change in operating personnel. Prilicla, Murchison, and Naydrad will still be there, remember. And Danalta . . . Well, with two empaths on the team, one of whom has muscles, can change shape at will, and get into normally inaccessible areas of a wrecked ship, there might even be an improvement in the rescue times.

"Second, there is Prilicla. You know as well as I do that it is one of our best Senior Physicians. But, for purely psychological and evolutionary reasons, it is incredibly timid, cowardly, and utterly lacking in self-assertion. Placing it in a position where it has overall responsibility and authority, at the site of a disaster, will accustom it to the idea of giving orders and making decisions without help from superiors. I realize that its orders may not sound like orders, and that they will be obeyed because nobody will want to hurt its feelings by objecting. But in time it should acquire the habit of command, and during the periods between rescue missions the habit will carry over to its work in the hospital. You agree?"

Conway tried to smile as he said, "I'm glad our little friend isn't here because my emotional radiation is anything but pleasant. But I agree."

"Good," the Major said. He went on briskly. "Third, there is Senior Physician Conway. We should be striving for objectivity in this matter, which is the reason why I am referring to you in the third person. He is a strange character in some ways, and has been since he joined us. A bit of a brat and very sure of himself in the early days, but he showed promise. In spite of this he remained a loner, didn't mix socially, and seemed to prefer the company of his extraterrestrial colleagues. Psychologically suspect behavior, that, but it conferred distinct advantages in a multispecies hospital where—"

"But Murchison isn't..." Conway began.

"...An extraterrestrial," O'Mara finished for him. "I realize that. The processes of senile decay are not so advanced in me that I would fail to notice that she is an Earth-human DBDG female, and then some. But apart from Murchison, your close friends are people like the Kelgian charge nurse Naydrad, the Melfan Senior Edanelt, Prilicla, and, of course, that SNLU dietician with the unpronounceable name from Level 302, and even Diagnostician Thornnastor. This is highly significant."

"What does it signify?" Conway asked, wishing desperately that the other would stop talking and give him time to think.

"You should be able to see that for yourself," O'Mara said sharply, then went on. "Add to this the fact that Conway has performed excellently over the years, has seen many important and unusual cases through to their successful conclusions, and has not been afraid to take personal responsibility for his professional decisions. And now there are indications that he may be losing his fine edge.

"It isn't serious as yet," the psychologist went on quickly before Conway could react. "In fact, neither his colleagues nor the man himself has noticed it, and there is no diminution of professional competence. But I have been studying his case very closely, and it has been apparent to me for some time that Conway is slipping into a rut, and must..."

"A *rut*! In this place?" Conway laughed in spite of himself.

"All things are relative," O'Mara said irritably. "Let us call it the increasingly routine response to the completely unexpected, if rut is too simple for you. But to resume, it is my considered opinion that this person requires a complete change of assignment and duties. This change should be preceded by the immediate removal from the ambulance ship responsibilities, some minor psychiatric assistance, and a period of mental reappraisal..."

"Agonizing reappraisal," Conway said, laughing again without knowing why. "Reappraisals are always supposed to be agonizing."

O'Mara studied him intently for a moment, then he exhaled slowly through his nose. Caustically, he said, "I don't approve of unnecessary suffering, Conway, but if you want to agonize while you're reappraising, feel free."

The Major's normally abrasive manner had returned, Conway noted. Apparently O'Mara no longer regarded him as a patient—which was pleasantly, or rather unpleasantly, reassuring. But his mind was fairly seething as it tried to assimilate and consider all the implications of this sudden and dramatic change in his situation, and he knew that he was temporarily incapable of responding coherently.

"I need time to think about this," he said.

"Naturally," O'Mara said.

"And I'd like to spend some time on *Rhabwar* to advise Prilicla on—"

"No!" O'Mara's open hand slapped the desk top. "Prilicla will have to learn to do the job in its own way, as you had to do, for the best results. You will stay away from the ambulance ship and not speak to the Cinrusskin except to wish it goodbye and good luck. In fact, I want you out of this hospital as quickly as possible. There is a Monitor Corps scoutship on courier duty leaving in thirty hours from now, so you won't have time for long goodbyes.

"I do not believe," he went on sardonically, "that there is any way that I can stop you saying a long goodbye to Murchison. Prilicla will already have broken the news of your imminent departure to her, and I can't think of anyone who could break it more gently, since it has been told what is going to happen to you over the next few months."

"I wish," Conway said sourly, "that somebody would tell *me*."

"Very well," the Chief Psychologist said, sitting back in his chair. "You are being assigned for an indefinite period to a planet which, in its most widely used language, is called Goglesk. They have a problem there. I don't know the details, but you will have plenty of time to brief yourself on it when you arrive, if it interests you. In this case you will not be expected to solve the problem; you will simply rest and—"

O'Mara's intercom buzzed, and a voice said, "Sorry, sir, but Doctor Fremvessith is here, early for its appointment. Shall I ask it to return later?"

"That's the PVGJ for the Kelgian tape erasure," O'Mara replied. "There are problems there. No, ask it to wait and administer sedation if necessary."

To Conway he went on. "As I was saying, while you are on Goglesk I want you to take things easy and think very carefully about your professional future, and take plenty of time to decide what you want to do or not do at Sector General. To assist the process, I'll provide some medication designed to enhance the memory and aid dream recall. There are no-long-term side effects. If you are going to take a mental inventory, the least I can do is supply a light for the darker recesses."

"But *why*?" Conway said, and suddenly he was not at all sure that he wanted the answer.

O'Mara was watching him intently, his mouth a tight, expressionless line, but the look in his eyes was sympathetic. He said, "You are beginning to realize the purpose of this meeting at last, Conway. But to save wear and tear on your overworked brain, I'll make it simple for you.

"The hospital is giving you the chance," he ended very seriously, "to try for Diagnostician."

A Diagnostician!...

Many times Conway had had the disquieting experience of having his mind shared with an alien alter ego, as had the majority of the medics at Sector General. He had even, for one relatively short period, had his mind apparently taken over by several extraterrestrials. But after that experience O'Mara had spent several days putting the mental pieces of the original Conway personality together again.

The problem was that although the hospital was equipped to treat every known form of intelligent life, no single person could hold in his or its mind even a fraction of the physiological data necessary for this purpose. Surgical dexterity was a product of experience and training, but the complete physiological information on a patient had to be furnished by means of an Educator tape, which was simply the brain record of some great medical genius belonging to the same or a similar species to that of the patient being treated.

If an Earth-human doctor had to treat a Kelgian patient, he took a DBLF physiology tape until treatment was completed, after which the tape was erased. The exceptions to this rule were the Senior Physicians of proven stability with teaching duties, and the Diagnosticians.

A Diagnostician was one of the medical *elite*, a being whose mind was considered stable enough to retain permanently six, seven, and in some cases ten physiology tapes simultaneously. To the data-crammed minds of the Diagnosticians were given the initiation and direction of original research in xenological medicine in addition to the practice and teaching of their considerable art.

But the tapes did not impart only the physiological data—the complete memory and personality of the entity who had possessed that knowledge was transferred as well. In effect a Diagnostician subjected himself or itself voluntarily to an extreme form of multiple schizophrenia. The entities apparently sharing one's mind could be aggressive, unpleasant individuals—geniuses were rarely charming people—with all sorts of peeves and phobias. Usually these did not become apparent during the course of an operation or treatment. Often the worst times were when the possessor of the tape was relaxing, or sleeping.

Alien nightmares, Conway had been told, were really nightmarish. And alien sexual fantasies or wish-fulfillment dreams were enough to make the person concerned wish, if he was capable of wishing coherently for anything, that he were dead. Conway swallowed.

"A response of some kind is called for," O'Mara said sarcastically, his manner indicating that he was back to being his usual, unlovable self and that the Conway interview was no longer a matter for concern. "Unless that gape is an attempt at nonverbal communication?"

"I... I need time to think about it," Conway said.

"You will have plenty of time to think about it," O'Mara said, standing up and looking pointedly at the desk chronometer, "on Goglesk."

Chapter 4

THE officers of the Monitor Corps scoutship *Trennelgon* knew Conway, both by reputation and by the fact that on three separate occasions he had given instructions to their communications officer during the search and retrieval operation on the widely scattered life capsules of the gigantic coil-ship belonging to the CRLT group-entity.

Virtually every scoutship in three Galactic Sectors had been called on to assist in that operation, and Conway had communicated with the majority of them at some stage, but this tenuous connection made *Trennelgon*'s crew act toward him as if he were a famous relative. So much so that there was no time to think, or feel morbid, or do anything but respond to their friendly curiosity regarding *Rhabwar* and its rescue missions until he began yawning uncontrollably in their faces.

He was told that the trip would require only two Jumps and that they were estimating arrival in the Goglesk system in just under ten hours, after which he was reluctantly allowed to retire.

But when he stretched out on the narrow Service bunk, it was inevitable that he would start thinking of Murchison, who was not stretched out beside him. And his recollections were sharp and clear as they always were of anything they had said or done together, so that O'Mara's memory-enhancing medication was superflous.

She had begun by discussing the implications of Prilicla's new appointment and the effect of Danalta's shape-changing faculty on the established rescue procedures. Only gradually had she worked the conversation around to Conway's possible advancement to Diagnostician. It had been obvious that she was as reluctant to bring up the subject as Conway had been, but Murchison was less of a moral coward.

"Prilicla has no doubt about you making it," he heard her saying again, "and neither have I. But if you were unable to adjust, or could not for some reason accept the position, it is still a high professional compliment to have been considered."

Conway did not reply, and she turned toward him, raising herself on one elbow. "Don't worry about it. You'll be gone for a few weeks, maybe months, and you'll hardly even miss me."

They both knew that was untrue. He looked up at her faintly smiling but concerned features and said, "As a Diagnostician I might not be the same person anymore. That's what is worrying me. I might end up not feeling the same toward *you*."

"I'll make damned sure that you do!" she said fiercely. More quietly, she went on, "Thornnastor has been a Diagnostician for nearly thirty years. I've had to work very closely with it as my head of department, and apart from gossiping and purveying information on all and sundry on the sexual misdemeanors of every species on the hospital staff, no serious personality changes have been apparent to . . ."

". . . A non-Tralthan like you," Conway finished for her.

It was her turn to be silent. He went on. "A few years back I had a multiple carapacial fracture on a Melfan. It was a lengthy procedure, done in stages, so that I had the ELNT tape riding me for three days. The Melfans have a great appreciation of physical beauty, so long as the physique concerned is exoskeletal and has at least six legs.

"Assisting me was OR Nurse Hudson," he continued. "You know Hudson? By the time the op was completed, I was much impressed with Hudson, and I and my Melfan alter ego were regarding her as a very pleasant personality, professionally most competent, but physically as a shapeless and unlovely bag of dough. I'm worried that—"

"Some members of her own species," Murchison put in sweetly, "also regard Hudson as a shapeless and unlovely bag—"

"Now, now," Conway said.

"I know, I'm being catty. I'm worried about that, too, and sorry that I cannot fully appreciate the problems you will be facing, because the Educator tapes are not for the likes of me."

She drew her features into a mock scowl and tried to reproduce the deep, rasping voice of O'Mara at its most bitingly sarcastic as she went on. "Absolutely not, Pathologist Murchison! I am well aware that the Educator tapes would assist you in your work. But you and the other females or extraterrestrial female equivalents on the staff will have to continue using your brains, such as they are, unaided. It is regrettable, but you females have a deep, ineradicable and sex-based aversion, a form of hyperfastidiousness, which will not allow you to share your minds with an alien personality which is unaffected by your sexual..."

The effort of maintaining the bass voice became too much for her, and she broke into a fit of coughing.

Conway laughed in spite of himself, then said pleadingly, "But what should I, what should we, *do*?"

She placed her hand lightly on his chest and leaned closer. Reassuringly, she said, "It might not be as bad as we think. I cannot imagine anyone or anything changing you if you don't want to be changed. You're far too stubborn, so I suppose we have to give it a try. But right now we should forget it and get some sleep."

She smiled down at him and added, "Eventually."

He had been given the supernumerary's position on the control deck—a courtesy not often offered to non-Service personnel—and was watching the main screen when *Trennelgon* emerged from hyperspace in the Goglesk system. The planet itself was a bluish, cloud-streaked globe similar in all respects, at this distance, to all the other worlds of the Federation which supported warm-blooded oxygen-breathing life. But Conway's primary interest was in the world's intelligent life-forms, and as diplomatically as possible he made that clear.

The Captain, an Orligian Monitor Corps Major called Sachan-Li, growled at him apologetically while its translator annunciated the words, "I'm sorry, Doctor. We know nothing of them, or of the planet itself beyond the perimeter of the landing area. We were pulled off survey duty to take the available Goglesk language data to the master translator in Sector General for processing, and to bring you and the translator program back here.

"Having you on board, Doctor," the Captain went on, "was a very welcome break in the monotony of a six-month mapping mission in Sector Ten, and I hope we didn't give you too hard a time with all our questions."

"Not at all, Captain," Conway said. "Is the perimeter guarded?"

"Only by wire netting," Sachan-Li replied. "To keep the nonintelligent grazers and scavengers from being cooked by our tail-blasts. The natives visit the base sometimes, I hear, but I've never seen one."

Conway nodded, then turned to watch the screen where the major natural features of the planet were becoming visible. He did not speak for several minutes, because Sachan-Li and the other officers—a diminutive, red-furred Nidian and two Earth-humans—were engaged in the prelanding checks. He watched as the world overflowed the edges of the screen and its surface changed gradually from being a vertical wall ahead of them to the ground below.

Trennelgon, in its hypersonic glider configuration, shuddered its way through the upper atmosphere, slowing as it lost altitude. Oceans, mountains, and green and yellow grasslands swept past below them, still looking normal and familiar and Earth-like. Then the horizon dropped suddenly below the bottom edge of the screen. They climbed, lost velocity, and began dropping and decelerating tail-first for a landing.

"Doctor," Sachan-Li said after they had touched down, "would you mind delivering this language program to the base commander? We are supposed to drop you and take off at once."

"Not at all," Conway said, slipping the package into a tunic pocket.

"Your personal gear is inside the air lock, Doctor," the Captain said. "It was a pleasure meeting you."

They did not take off at once, but the heat from *Trennelgon*'s tail-flare as it took off half a mile behind him warmed the back of Conway's neck. He continued walking toward the three closely grouped hemispheres which were the accommodation normally used for a non-permanent base with minimum personnel. He had not taken a gravity float for his gear, because his belongings fitted easily into a backpack and a large handgrip, but the late evening sun was warm, and he decided to put down his grip for a moment and rest—the degree of urgency on this job, after all, was zero.

It was then that the strangeness hit him.

He looked down at the earth which was not of the Earth; at the grass which was subtly different from that of his home world; and at the undergrowth, wildflowers, vegetation, and distant trees which, although looking superfically similar, were the products of a completely different evolutionary process. He shivered briefly despite the heat as the feeling of *intrusion* which he always felt on these occasions washed over-him, and he thought of the less-subtle differences which would soon become manifest in this world's dominant life-form. He lifted the handgrip and began walking again.

When he was still a few minutes away from the largest of the three bubble buildings, its main entrance slid open and a figure came hurrying out to meet him. The man was wearing the uniform and insignia of a Lieutenant in the Monitor Corps's Cultural Contact section, and was capless—he was either a naturally sloppy person or one of the Corps's academics who had little time for worrying about their uniforms or any other clothing they might be wearing. He was well built, with fair, receding hair and highly mobile features, and he spoke when they were still more than three meters apart.

"I'm Wainright," he said quickly. "You must be the Sector General medic, Conway. Did you bring the language program?"

Conway nodded and reached into his tunic pocket with his left hand while proffering the right to the Lieutenant. Wainright drew back quickly.

"No, Doctor," he said apologetically but firmly. "You must get out of the habit of shaking hands here, or of making any other kind of physical contact. It isn't done on this planet, except in certain rare circumstances, and the natives find it, well, disquieting if they see us doing it. But that bag looks heavy. If you place it on the ground and move away, I'll be happy to carry it for you."

"I can manage, thanks," Conway said absently. There were several questions lining up in his mind, jostling each other for priority in vocalization. He began to walk toward the bubble with the Lieutenant at his side, but still separated from him by a distance of three meters.

"That tape will be very useful, Doctor," Wainright said. "Our translation computer should be able to handle the language now, with a lot fewer misunderstandings. But we weren't expecting someone from Sector General to be sent out so quickly. Thanks for coming, Doctor."

Conway waved away the thanks with his free hand and said, "Don't expect me to solve your problem, whatever it is, as easily as all that. I've been sent here to observe the situation, and think about it, and . . ." He thought of the principal reason O'Mara had sent him to Goglesk, to think about his future at the hospital, but he did not feel like telling the Lieutenant about that just yet, so he ended, ". . . And to rest."

Wainright looked at him sharply, his expression registering concern. But it was obvious that the Lieutenant was much too polite to ask Conway why a Senior Physician from the Federation's largest hospital, where every conceivable medical and psychological treatment was available, had come here to rest.

Instead, he said, "Speaking of rest, Doctor, where were you on ship time? Is it after breakfast, the middle of your day, or long past your bedtime? Would you like to rest now? It is late afternoon here, and we can easily talk in the morning."

Conway said, "I slept well and wakened less than two hours ago, and I want to talk now. In fact, if you don't stop me asking questions, Lieutenant, it is you who are going to miss a lot of sleep."

"I won't stop you, Doctor." Wainright laughed. "I don't want to suggest that my assistants are not always entertaining people, or that their digital dexterity is sometimes used to influence the laws of probability while playing cards, but it will be nice having someone new to talk to. Besides, the natives disappear at sunset, and there is nothing to do except talk about them, and that hasn't gotten us very far up until now."

He entered the building in front of Conway. There was a narrow corridor inside with a nearby door which had the Lieutenant's name on it. Wainright stopped in front of the door, looked quickly in both directions, and then asked Conway for the tape.

"Come in, Doctor," he said then, sliding open the door and walking across the large office to a desk which had a translator terminal on its top. Conway looked around the office, which was lit by the warm, orange light of the near-to-setting sun. Most of the floor space was empty of furniture, with the desk, filing and retrieval systems, projection equipment, and even the visitors' chairs crowded against the wall opposite to the window. Beside the window there was a large, dumpy cactuslike plant whose spikes and hair were richly colored in a pattern which seemed less random the more he looked at it.

He became aware of a faint odor coming from the planet, a smell which seemed to be a combination of musk and peppermint, and he moved across the office for a closer examination.

The cactus moved back.

"This is Khone." The Lieutenant switched on the translator. He indicated the doctor and said, "This is Conway. He, too, is a healer."

While Wainright was talking, the translator had been producing a harsh, sighing sound which had to be the being's language. Conway thought for a moment, discarding in turn a number of polite, diplomatic phrases his own species used on occasions like this. It was better to be positive and unambiguous.

"I wish you well, Khone," he said.

"And I, you," the extraterrestrial said.

Wainright said quickly, "You should know, Doctor, that names are used only once during a conversation for the purposes of introduction, identification, or recognition. After the initial use, try to speak as impersonally as possible so as to avoid giving offense. Later, we can discuss this matter more fully. This Gogleskan person has waited until nearly sunset just to meet you, but now..."

"...It must leave," the being ended.

The Lieutenant nodded and said, "A vehicle with a rear loading ramp has been provided, so that the passenger may board and travel while avoiding close physical proximity with the driver. The passenger will be home long before dark."

"Consideration has been shown," the Gogleskan said as it turned to go, "and gratitude is expressed."

During the conversation Conway had been studying the extraterrestrial. The mass of unruly hair and spikes covering its erect, ovoid body were less irregular in their size and placing than he had at first thought. The body hair had mobility, though not the high degree of flexibility and rapid mobility of the Kelgian fur, and the spikes, some of which were extremely flexible and grouped together to form a digital cluster, gave evidence of specialization. The other spikes were longer, stiffer, and some of them seemed to be partially atrophied, as if they had been evolved for natural defense, but the reason for their presence had long since gone. There were also a number of long, pale tendrils lying amid the multicolored hair covering the cranial area, but the purpose of these was unclear.

There was a thin band of dull metal encircling the domelike neckless head, and a few inches below the metal band were two widely spaced and recessed eyes. Its voice seemed to come from a number of small, vertical breathing orifices which encircled its waist. The being sat on a flat, muscular pad, and it was not until it turned to leave that Conway saw that it had legs as well.

These members were stubbly and concertinalike, and when the four of them were in use they increased the height of the being by several inches. He also saw that it had two additional eyes at the back of its head—obviously this species had had to be very watchful in prehistoric times—and he suddenly realized the purpose of the metal band. It was used to suspend a corrective lens over one of the Gogleskan's eyes.

Despite the physical configuration the being was a warm-blooded oxygen-breather and not an intelligent vegetable, and Conway classified it physiologically as FOKT. As it was leaving the room, it paused in the doorway, and a group of its digits twitched briefly.

"Be lonely," it said.

Chapter 5

GOGLESK had been a borderline case so far as the Cultural Contact people were concerned. Full contact with such a technologically backward culture was dangerous, because when the Monitor Corps ships dropped out of their skies, they could not be sure whether they were giving the Gogleskans a future goal toward which to aim or a devastating inferiority complex. But the natives, in spite of their backwardness in the physical sciences and the obscure racial psychosis which forced them to remain so, were psychologically stable as individuals, and the planet had not known war for many thousands of years.

The easiest course would have been to withdraw and leave the Gogleskan culture to continue as it had been doing since the dawn of its history, and write their problem off as being insoluble. Instead, Cultural Contact had made one of its very rare compromises.

They had established a small base to accommodate a handful of observers, their supplies and equipment, which included a flyer and two general-purpose ground vehicles. The purpose of the base was to observe and gather data, nothing more. But Wainright and his team had developed a liking for those sorely tried natives and, contrary to their instructions, wanted to do more.

Problems had been encountered in obtaining accurate translations with their relatively simple equipment—the Gogleskan word-sounds were made by producing minor variations in the quantity of air expelled through four separate breathing orifices, and several potentially dangerous misunderstandings had occurred. They had decided to send their language data for checking and reprocessing to the big multitranslation computer at Sector General. So as not to disobey their instructions directly, they accompanied the material with a brief statement on the Gogleskan situation and a request to the hospital's Department of E-T Psychology for information on any similar life-form or condition which Sector General might have encountered in the past.

". . . But instead of sending information," the Lieutenant went on as he lifted the groundcar over a fallen tree which was blocking the path they were following through the forest, "they sent us Senior Physician Conway, who is—"

"Here simply to observe," Conway broke in, "and to rest."

Wainright laughed. "You didn't rest much during the past four days."

"That's because I was too busy observing," Conway said drily. "But I wish Khone had come back to see me. You think I should visit it now?"

"That could be the correct behavior in these circumstances," the other replied. "They have some odd rules and, intensely individualistic as they are, they may consider two consecutive and uninvited visits to be an unwarranted intrusion. If a person's first visit is welcome, you may simply be expected to return it. We're entering the inhabited area now."

Gradually the forest floor had become clear of small trees and bushes, leaving only a thin carpet of grasslike vegetation between the massive trunks which served as the main structural supports for the Gogleskan dwellings. To Conway they looked like the log cabins of ancient history—but roofless because the overhanging branches provided all the necessary weather protection—and the wide variation in style and quality of workmanship made it clear that they had been built by their occupiers rather than by an organization specializing in home construction.

If a species' progress was based on group and tribal cooperation, it was easy to understand why there had been so little of it on Goglesk. But why, Conway wondered for the hundredth time since his arrival, did they refuse to cooperate with each other when they were so obviously intelligent, friendly, and nonaggressive?

"And highly accident-prone," the Lieutenant said, making Conway realize that he had been thinking aloud. "This looks like a good place to ask questions."

"Right," Conway said, opening the canopy. They had drawn level with three Gogleskans who were grouped, very loosely, around one of their spindly legged draught animals and the contraption of unknown purpose to which it was harnessed. He went on. "Thanks for the ride, Lieutenant. I'll wander around and talk to a few people in addition to Khone, if I can find it, then walk back to base. If I get lost I'll call you."

Wainright shook his head and cut the vehicle's power, letting it settle to the ground. He said, "You aren't in your hospital now, where everybody is either a medic or a patient. The rule is that we go around in pairs. There is no danger of giving offense provided you don't move too close to them, or me. After you, Doctor."

Followed at a distance by the Lieutenant, Conway climbed down and walked toward the three natives, stopping several paces before he came to the nearest one. Not looking at anyone in particular, he said, "Is it possible to be given directions to the dwelling place of the entity Khone?"

One of the Gogleskans indicated the direction with two of its long spikes. "If the vehicle proceeds in that direction," it sighed at them, "a clearing will be encountered. More precise directions may be obtained there."

"Gratitude is expressed," Conway said, and returned to the groundcar.

The clearing turned out to be a wide crescent of grass and rocky outcroppings on the shore of a large inland lake, judging by the absence of sand and the small size of the waves. There were several jetties projecting into the deeper water, and most of the small craft tied alongside had thin smokestacks as well as sails. The buildings clustered near the water's edge were tall, three or four stories high, built of stone and wood, and with ascending ramps running up and around all four faces, so that from certain angles they looked like thin pyramids, an effect which was enhanced by their tall, conical roofs.

If it had not been for the all-pervading noise and smoke, the overall effect would have been one of picturesque, medieval charm.

"It is the town's manufacturing and food-processing center," the Lieutenant said. "I've seen it several times from the flyer. The fish smell will hit you in a minute."

"It's hitting me already," Conway said. He was thinking that if this was what passed for an industrial area, then the healer, Khone, was probably the equivalent of a factory medic. He was looking forward to talking to the being again, and perhaps seeing it at work.

They were directed past a large building whose stonework and wooden beams were smoke-blackened and still smelling of a recent fire, to the edge of the lake where a large boat had sunk at its moorings. Opposite the wreck there was a low, partially roofed structure with a stream running under it. From their elevated position on the groundcar they could see into a mazelike system of corridors and tiny rooms which was Khone's dwelling and, presumably, an adjoining hospital.

A Gogleskan patient was having something done to its

breathing orifices—a nonsurgical investigation, Conway saw, using long wooden probes and dilators, followed by the oral administration of medication also by a long-handled instrument. The patient occupied one cubicle during this procedure and the healer another. It was several minutes before Khone came outside and acknowledged their presence.

"Interest is felt," Conway said when the three of them were on the ground and standing at the points of an invisible equilateral triangle more than three meters on the side, "in the subject of healing on Goglesk. Comparisons of other-world knowledge and treatments might be made, of illnesses, injuries, and nonphysical disorders, and particularly of surgical procedures and anatomical studies."

Khone's center of attention was in the space between Wainright and Conway as it replied, "There is no curative surgery on Goglesk. Anatomical work is possible only on cadavers stripped of stings and residual poisons. Personal physical contact, except for the purposes of procreation or the care of nonadults, is dangerous for both the healer and patient. A certain minimum distance is essential for the performance of my work."

"But *why*?" Conway said, moving instinctively toward the healer. Then he saw that Khone's fur was agitated and that the spikes all over its body were twitching. He turned toward the Lieutenant, ostensibly addressing Wainright when he spoke.

"An instrument in my possession enables a trained healer to observe the position and workings of internal organs and to chart the locations of bones and principal blood vessels," Conway said, and withdrew the scanner from its pouch at his side.

He began passing it slowly along his other arm, then moved it to his head, chest, and abdomen, describing in his most impersonal, lecturing voice the function of the organs, bone structure, and associated musculature revealed on the scanner's screen. Then he pulled the instrument's telescoping handle to full extension and moved it closer to Khone.

"The instrument provides this information without

touching the patient's body," he added, "if that should be a requirement."

Khone had moved a little closer while he had been demonstrating the scanner, and the being had rotated its body so that the eye with the spectacle could be brought to bear on the instrument. Conway had angled the screen so that the Gogleskan could see its own internal structure while he could not. But he had also set the scanner to record so that he would be able to study the material later.

He watched the healer's spikes twitching and the long, multicolor hair rising up stiffly to lie flat again, several times in a minute. Some of the colored strands lay at right angles to the others, giving a plaid effect. The breathing orifices were making an urgent, hissing sound, but Khone was not moving away from the scanner, and gradually the being was growing calmer.

"Enough," it said. Surprisingly, it looked straight at Conway with its ridiculous, bespectacled eye. There was a long silence, during which it was obvious that the Gogleskan was coming to a decision.

"On this world," it said finally, "the art of the healer is a unique one, and the probability exists that this is true in other places. A healer may, while treating a patient, explore delicate areas and states of mind, and pry into material which is distressful or even shameful, but invariably personal. This normally forbidden and dangerous behavior is allowed because the speaker may not speak of anything learned, except to another healer who is being consulted in the interests of the patient..."

Hippocrates, Conway thought, *could not have said it better*.

"...And it might be possible," Khone went on, "to discuss such matters with an off-world healer. But it must be understood that these matters are for the ears only of another healer."

"As a layman," the Lieutenant said, smiling, "I know when I'm not wanted. I'll wait in the groundcar."

Conway got down on one knee so that his eyes were on a level with those of the Gogleskan. If they were to speak together as equals, he thought, the process might be aided considerably if Conway did not tower over the other healer, whose hair and spikes were again twitching in agitation. They were less than two meters apart now. He decided to take the initiative.

He had to be careful not to overawe Khone with gratuitous accounts of medical superscience, so he began by describing the work of Sector General in very simple terms, but continually emphasizing the multispecies aspects and stressing the high degree of professional cooperation required for its performance. From there he worked gradually around to the subject of cooperation in general and its importance in fields other than medicine.

"...Observations have been made," Conway went on, "which suggest that progress here has been retarded for reasons which, considering the high intelligence of individual Gogleskans, are not clear. Is an explanation possible?"

"Progress is impossible because cooperation is impossible," Khone replied, and suddenly it became less impersonal. "Healer Conway, we are constantly fighting ourselves and the behavior patterns imposed on us by survival instincts evolved, I suspect, at the time when we were the nonintelligent food source of every sea-dwelling predator on Goglesk. To successfully fight these instincts requires self-discipline in our thinking and actions if we are not to lose the very modest, nay, backward, level of culture that we now possess."

"If the exact nature of the problem could be explained in detail," Conway began, and then he, too, slipped into a more personal mode, "I would like to help you, Healer Khone. It might be that a completely strange healer, one who has a completely new and perhaps even an alien viewpoint, could suggest a solution which would not otherwise have occurred to the entities concerned..."

He broke off because an irregular, urgent drumming sound had started up from somewhere further inland. Khone drew away from him again. "Apologies are tendered for the immediate departure," it said loudly. "There is urgent work for a healer."

Wainright leaned out of the groundcar. "If Khone is in

a hurry . . ." he began, then corrected himself. "If rapid transport is required, it is available."

The rear storage compartment was already open and the loading ramps extending groundward.

They reached the scene of the accident after ten minutes of the most hair-raising driving that Conway had ever experienced—the Gogleskan, probably because of its naturally slow method of ambulation, did not give directions for turning corners until they were abreast of the intersection concerned. By the time Wainright had grounded the vehicle beside the partly demolished three-story building indicated by Khone, Conway was wondering if for the first time in his adult life he would succumb to motion sickness.

But all subjective considerations were driven from his mind when he saw the casualties hobbling or tumbling down the cracked or slowly collapsing external ramps, or struggling out of the large, ground-level doorway which was partly blocked by fallen rubble. Their many-colored body hair was hidden beneath a layer of dust and wood splinters, and on a few of the bodies he could see the wet, red gleam of fresh wounds. But all of them were ambulatory, he saw as he jumped down from the vehicle, and they were all moving as fast as they could away from the damaged building to join the wide and surprisingly distant circle of onlookers.

Suddenly he caught sight of a Gogleskan shape protruding from the debris around the doorway, and heard the untranslatable sounds it was making.

"Why are they standing there?" he yelled at Khone, waving toward the onlookers. "Why don't they *help* it?"

"Only a healer may closely approach another Gogleskan when it is in distress," Khone said as its tiny manipulators drew thin wooden rods from a pouch strapped to its middle and began slotting them together. It added, "Or a person with sufficient mental self-control not to be affected by that distress."

Conway was following the healer as it moved toward the casualty. He said, "Perhaps a being of a completely different species could bring to bear on the case the required degree of clinical detachment."

"No," Khone said firmly. "Physical contact or even a close approach must be avoided."

The Gogleskan's rods had fitted together into a set of long-handled tongs to which, as the examination of the casualty proceeded, Khone added a series of interchangeable probes, spatulas, and lenses which were later substituted for fine brushes and swabs soaked in what must have been antiseptics for cleaning the wounds. This was followed by suturing of the larger incisions, using an ingenious device clipped to the end of the tongs. But the treatment was superficial and very, very slow.

Conway quickly extended the telescopic handle of his scanner until it was the same length as Khone's tongs, then went down onto his hands and knees and pushed the instrument toward the healer.

"Internal injuries may be present," he said. "This instrument will reveal them."

Thanks were not expressed—probably Khone was too busy to be polite—but the Gogleskan laid down its tongs at once and began using Conway's scanner. Its manipulators were awkward at first, but very soon they had adapted to the grips which had been designed for Earth-human fingers so that Khone began varying the focus and magnification in a manner that was almost expert.

"There is minor bleeding from the buried section of the body," the Gogleskan said a few minutes later. "But it will be observed that the greatest danger to the casualty is the interruption of the blood supply to the cranial area, just here, which is caused by pressure from a wooden beam lying across and compressing the main cranial artery. This has also caused unconsciousness, which explains the lack of recent sounds and body movements which will also have been observed."

"Rescue procedure?" Conway asked.

"Rescue is not possible in the time available," Khone replied. "There is no knowledge regarding the time units used by the off-world healer, but the conditions will be terminal in approximately one-fiftieth of the time period between our dawn and dusk. However, the attempt must be made . . ."

Conway looked at Wainright, who said quietly, "About fifteen minutes."

". . . To immobilize the beam with a wedge," the Gogleskan went on, "and remove the rubble from under the casualty so that the being will subside into a position where the constriction from the beam will be removed. There is also the risk of a further collapse of the structure, so the removal of beings other than the casualty and its healer is urgently requested in the interest of their safety."

It returned the scanner to Conway long handle first, and when he took it back the Gogleskan began fitting soil-moving claws to its tongs.

Conway had the nightmarish feeling of being faced with a simple problem requiring a minimal amount of manual activity, and having both hands tied behind his back. It was impossible for him to stand by and watch an injured being die when there were so many ways that he could try to save it. And yet he had been expressly forbidden to go near the creature, even though its fellow Gogleskan knew that he wanted only to help. It was stupid, of course, but there had to be something in this species' culture which made sense of the apparent stupidity.

He looked helplessly at Wainright, and at the stocky, heavily muscled body which made the Lieutenant's coveralls look tight, and tried again.

"If a casualty is unconscious," he said desperately, "it should not be adversely affected by the close presence or touch of other beings. It might be possible for the off-worlders to lift the beam sufficiently high for the casualty to be drawn free."

"Many others are watching," Khone said, and its indecision was shown by the way it raised and then lowered its tongs. Then it fitted a new set of tips to them, produced a coil of light rope from somewhere, and began using the tongs to loop it around the casualty's feet. It went on. "Very well. But there are risks. And the casualty and its healer must not be closely approached by off-worlders, or be seen by others to make such an approach, no matter how well-intentioned it is."

Conway did not ask how close "closely" was as he preceded the Lieutenant into the wide, low entrance, each putting a shoulder under the beam which was supporting one side of it. No doubt the physical proximity of Wainright and Conway was offensive to the onlookers, but the doorway was shadowed and perhaps the watching Gogleskans could not see them clearly. Right then Conway was too busy pushing to care what they thought.

Dust and fine rubble rained down on them as they lifted their end of the beam by three, four, and then nearly six inches. But at the other end where the casualty was trapped, it rose by barely two inches. Khone's tongs had successfully looped the rope around the casualty's legs, and it had wrapped the other end several times around its own middle. It took up the slack, braced its feet, and leaned against the rope like the anchorman in a tug-of-war team, but without effect. The Gogleskan FOKT life-form was too lightly built and physiologically unsuited to the application of the required traction.

"Can you hold it up yourself for a moment?" Wainright asked, crouching suddenly and disappearing further into the entrance. "I can see something that might help us."

It seemed much longer than a moment while the Lieutenant dug among the rubble inside the entrance and the beam dug into Conway's shoulder. His straining back and leg muscles were knotted in a continual, fiery cramp. He blinked the sweat out of his eyes and saw that Khone had changed its approach to the problem. Instead of pulling continuously, it had begun returning as close as was allowable to the casualty and then waddling as fast as it could away from it until the rope was pulled taut, trying to jerk the other Gogleskan free.

With every jerk the injured FOKT moved a little, but some of the sutures had opened and it was bleeding freely again.

Every single vertebra in his back was being compressed into a single osseous column, Conway thought angrily, which any second now would break.

"*Hurry*, dammit!"

"I *am* hurrying," Khone said, forgetting to be impersonal.

"Coming," the Lieutenant said.

Wainright arrived with a short, thick piece of timber which he quickly wedged between the beam and the ground. Conway collapsed thankfully onto his knees, easing his maltreated shoulder and back, but only for a moment. The Lieutenant's idea was for them to lift with a few seconds of maximum effort, and then use the prop to keep from losing the extra height gained, repeating the process until the casualty could be pulled free.

It was a very good idea, but the intermittent falls of dust and rubble were becoming a steadily increasing shower. The casualty was almost free when there was a low rumble and the sound of splintering timber from inside the building.

"Get clear!" Khone shouted as it got ready to give one last, desperate jerk on the rope. But as the healer came to the end of its waddling run, the loop slipped off the casualty's feet and Khone went tumbling and rolling away, entangled in its own rescue rope.

Later, Conway was to spend a long and agonizing time wondering whether he had done the right or the wrong thing just then, but there was simply no time to evaluate and compare extraterrestrial social behavior with that of Earth-humans—he did it because he could not do anything else. He checked his stumbling run away from the collapsing entrance, turned and grabbed the unconscious FOKT casualty by the feet.

With his greater weight and strength it came away easily, and crouched double and moving backward, he dragged it clear of the subsiding building. As the dust began to settle, he pulled it gently onto a patch of soft grass. Nearly all of Khone's sutures had pulled free, and the casualty had acquired a number of new wounds, all of which were bleeding.

The being opened its eyes suddenly, stiffened, then began making a loud, continuous, hissing sound which wavered up and down in pitch so that at times it was almost a whistle.

"*No*!" Khone said urgently. "There is no danger! It is a healer, a friend! . . ."

But the irregular hissing and whistling grew louder, and Conway was aware that the circle of onlookers, no longer distant, had joined in. He could scarcely hear himself think. Khone was stumbling around the casualty, sometimes approaching to within a few inches, then moving away again, as if it was performing an intricate ritual dance.

"Yes," Conway said reassuringly, "I'm not an enemy. I pulled you out."

"You stupid, stupid healer!" Khone said, sounding angry as well as personal. "You ignorant off-worlder! Go *away*! . . ."

What happened then was one of the strangest sights Conway had ever witnessed, and at Sector General he had seen many of those. The casualty rolled and jerked itself to its feet, still emitting the undulating whistling noises. Khone had begun to make the same sound, and the long, stiff body hair on both beings was standing out straight, so that the plaid effect caused by the different colors lying at right angles to each other was lost. Suddenly Khone and the casualty touched and were instantly welded or, more accurately, tightly woven together where they had made contact.

The stiff hairs covering their sides had insinuated into and through each other, like the warp and weft of an old-time woven rug, and it was plain that no outside agency would be able to separate them without removing the hair of both creatures and probably the underlying tegument as well.

"Let's get out of here, Doctor," Wainright said from the top of the groundcar, pointing at the Gogleskans who were closing in from all sides.

Conway hesitated, watching a third FOKT join itself in the same incredible fashion to Khone and the casualty. The long spikes whose purpose he had not known were projecting stiffly from the cranium of every Gogleskan, and there was a bright yellow secretion oozing from the tips. As he climbed into the vehicle, one of the spikes tore the fabric of his coveralls, but without penetrating the underlying clothing or skin.

While the Lieutenant moved the vehicle to higher ground for a better view of what was going on, Conway used his analyzer on the traces of yellow secretion which had been left along the edges of the tear in his suit. He was able to calculate that the contents of one of those stings introduced directly into the bloodstream would be instantly disabling, and that three or more of them would be fatal.

The Gogleskans were joining themselves into a group-entity which was growing larger by the minute. Individual FOKTs were hurrying from nearby buildings, moored ships, and even from the surrounding trees to add themselves to this great, mobile, spiky carpet which crawled around large buildings and over small ones as if it did not know or care what it was doing. In its wake it left a trail of smashed equipment, vehicles, dead animals, and even one capsized ship. The vessel had been tied up, and when the periphery of the group-entity had stumbled on board it had flipped onto its side, smashing the masts and superstructure against the jetty.

But the Gogleskans who had fallen into the water did not seem to be inconvenienced, Conway saw, and the movement of the land-based constituents of the group-entity pulled them out again within a few minutes.

"They're not blind," Conway said, aghast at the wholesale destruction. He stood on his bucket seat to get a better view and went on. "There are enough unobscured eyes around the periphery for them to see where they're going, but they seem to have great difficulty making up their mind. Oh, man, they're fairly wrecking that settlement. Can you put up the flyer and get me a detailed, high-level record of this?"

"Can do," the Lieutenant said. He spoke briefly into his communicator, then went on. "It isn't making straight for us, Doctor, but it's trying to get nearer. We'd better change position."

"No, wait," Conway said, gripping the edge of the open canopy and leaning out, the better to see the edge of the group-entity which had stumbled to within six meters' distance. Dozens of eyes regarded him coldly, and the long, yellow-tipped stings were like a thinly stubbled hayfield. "They are hostile, yet Khone itself was friendly. Why?"

His voice was almost drowned by the rushing, whistling sound made by the group, a sound which their translators did not register. But somewhere in that unintelligible mush there was a whisper of intelligence trying to fight its way out, the voice of the Gogleskan healer.

"Go away," it said. "Go away."

Conway had to drop quickly into his seat before Wainright closed the canopy on him and they moved away. Angrily, the Lieutenant said, "You can't *do* anything!"

Chapter 6

THERE was no need for the memory-enhancing medication which Conway had been taking since leaving Sector General to recall the incident—it was there in his mind, complete in every detail. And there was no arguing against the evidence, no escaping the damning conclusion that he alone was responsible for the whole sorry mess.

The vision tapes from the flyer had shown an immediate decrease in the destructive activity of the rampaging Gogleskans as soon as the groundcar carrying Wainright and Conway had left the scene. And within an hour the group-entity had fragmented into its individual members, who had stood immobile, widely separated from each other and giving the impression that they were suffering from extreme exhaustion.

He had gone over the visual material again and again, together with his scanner's playback of the self-examination by Khone and the later material on the FOKT whose rescue had precipitated the fusion of all the Gogleskans in the area. He tried to find a clue, a mere indication, the most tenuous of hints which would explain the reason for the FOKTs' incredible reaction to his touching one of their number, but without success.

At one stage the thought came that he was here to rest, to clear his mind so that he could make important decisions regarding his future. The Gogleskan situation was a nonurgent problem which, according to O'Mara, he could think about or ignore. But he could *not* ignore it, because, apart from making it fractionally worse, he had been presented with a puzzle so alien that even his long experience of extraterrestrial behavior and thought processes at the hospital was not of much help.

As an individual, Khone had been so *normal.*

Irritably he dropped into his bunk, still holding his scanner at eye level and trying to squeeze some meaning out of the FOKT recordings. In theory it was impossible to feel discomfort in a bunk with gravity controls set to a tiny fraction of one Earth-G, but Conway wriggled and tossed and managed to feel very uncomfortable indeed.

He was able to trace the shallow roots of the four FOKT stings, which at the time Khone had been examining itself had been lying flat against the upper cranium and partially concealed by the surrounding hair, and chart the positions of the fine ducts which connected the spikes to the poison sac which supplied them. There was also a nerve linkage between the base of the brain and the muscles for erecting the stings and for compressing the reservoir of venom, but he had no idea of the kind of stimulus which would trigger this activity. Neither had he any ideas regarding the function of the long, silvery strands which lay among the coarser cranial hair.

His first thought, that they were simply an indication of advancing age, had to be revised when closer study showed that the follicle structure was completely unlike that of the surrounding hair and that they, like the stings, had underlying muscle and nerve connections which gave them the capability of independent movement. Unlike the stings, they were much larger, finer, and more flexible.

Unfortunately he could not trace the subdermal nerve connections, if such were present, because his scanner had not been set for such fine work. His intention had been simply to impress the Gogleskan healer by showing it pictures of its own major organs operating, and no amount of magnification during playback could bring up details which were not already there.

Even so, had it not been for the utterly strange behavior of the FOKTs, Conway would have been highly satisfied with the physiological data he had obtained. But in this case he was not satisfied. He badly wanted to meet Khone again and examine it more closely—both clinically and verbally.

After today's debacle the chance of that happening was small indeed.

"Go away!" Khone had told him from somewhere within that rampaging mob of Gogleskans. And the Lieutenant, too, had been angry when he had shouted, "You can't *do* anything!"

Conway knew that he had slipped into sleep when he became aware that he was no longer on Goglesk. His surroundings had changed, but they were still familiar, and the problems occupying his mind had become much simpler. He did not dream very often—or, as O'Mara was fond of reminding him, he dreamed as frequently as any other so-called intelligent being, but was fortunate in that he recalled very few of his dreams. This particular dream was pleasant, uncomplicated, and bore no relation to his present situation.

At least, so it seemed at first.

The chairs were enormous and had to be climbed into instead of being sat upon, and the big dining table, which was also hand-built, required him to stand on tiptoe if he was to see onto the deeply grained and highly polished planking of its top. That, thought the mature, dreaming Conway, placed him at the age of about eight.

Whether the effect was due to O'Mara's medication or

a psychological quirk which was all his own, Conway did not know, but he was viewing the dream as a mature and fully informed adult while his feelings about it were those of a not very happy eight-year-old.

His parents had been third-generation colonists on the mineral-rich, Earth-seeded world of Braemar which, at the time of their deaths, had been explored, tamed, and made safe—at least, so far as the areas occupied by the mining and agricultural towns and the single spaceport were concerned.

He had lived on the outskirts of that spaceport city, which was a great, sprawling complex of one- , two- , and three-story buildings, for all of his young life. He had not thought it strange that the log cabins greatly outnumbered the towering white blocks of the manufacturing complexes, the administration center, the spacefield buildings, and the hospital; or that the furniture, nonmetal household equipment, pottery, and ornaments were all home-produced. With his mature hindsight he knew that wood was plentiful and cheap on Braemar while imported Earth furniture and gadgetry were very expensive and, in any case, the colonists took pride in their own handiwork and wanted it no other way.

But the log cabins were powered and lit by modern fusion generators, and the hand-built furniture supported sophisticated vision transceivers whose chief purposes were, so far as the young Conway was concerned, to educate during the day and entertain in the evening. Ground and air transportation was also modern, fast, and as safe as it was possible to make it, and only very occasionally did a flyer drop out of the sky with the loss of all on board.

It was not the loss of his parents which was making him unhappy. He had been too young to remember them as anything but vague, comforting presences, and when they had been called to the emergency at the mine he had been left in the charge of a young couple who were close neighbors. He had remained with them until after the burial, when his father's oldest brother had taken him to live with his family.

His aunt and uncle had been kindly, responsible, and very busy people who were no longer young. Their own children were young adults, so except for a period of initial curiosity, they had very little time for him. Not so the grandmother of the house, Conway's great-grandmother, who had decided that the newly orphaned infant would be her sole responsibility.

She was incredibly old—anyone who dared ask her age did not do it a second time—and as fragile as a Cinrusskin, but was still physically and mentally active. She had been the first child born to the Braemar colony, and when Conway began taking an interest in such things, she had an endless supply of stories about those early days of the colony which were far more exciting, if perhaps a little less factual, than the material in the history tapes.

Without understanding what they had been talking about at the time, Conway had heard his uncle tell a visitor that the kid and the old lady got on very well together because they were the same mental age. Except when she chastised him, which was not very often and not at all during the later years, she was always good fun. She covered for him when accidents occurred which were not entirely his fault, and she defended his pet-pen when it began to grow from a small, wired-in enclosure in the back garden to something resembling a miniature wildlife park, although she was most insistent that he not acquire pets which he could not care for properly.

He had a few Earth pets as well as a collection of the small and harmless native Braemar Herbivores—who sometimes took sick, frequently injured themselves, and multiplied practically all the time. She had called up the relevant veterinary tapes for him—such material was considered too advanced for a child—and with her advice and by his using practically all of his nonstudy time the inhabitants of his pet-pen prospered and, much to his aunt and uncle's surprise, showed a fair profit when the word got around that he was a prime source of healthy garden and household pets for the neighborhood children.

The young Conway was kept much too busy to realize that he was a very lonely boy—until his great-grandmother and only friend suddenly lost interest in talking about his pets, and seemed to lose interest in him. The doctor began visiting her regularly, and then his aunt and uncle took it in turn to stay in the room with her night and day, and they forbade him even to see his only friend.

That was why he felt unhappy. And the adult Conway, remembering as well as reexperiencing the whole incident, knew that there was more unhappiness to come. The dream was about to become a nightmare.

They had forgotten to lock the door one evening, and when he sneaked into the bedroom he found his aunt sitting on a chair by the bedside with her chin on her chest, dozing. His great-grandmother was lying with her face turned toward him, her eyes and mouth wide open, but she did not speak and she did not seem to see him. As he moved toward the bed, he heard her harsh, irregular breathing, and he became aware of the smell. Suddenly he felt frightened, but he reached forward to touch the thin, wasted arm which lay outside the bedclothes. He was thinking that she might look at him or say something, or maybe even smile at him the way she had done only a few weeks ago.

The arm was *cold*.

The mature and medically experienced Conway knew that circulation had already failed at the extremities and that the old lady had only minutes to live, and the very young Conway knew it, too, without knowing why. Unable to stop himself, he tried to call her, and his aunt woke up. She looked at his grand-grandmother, then grabbed him tightly by the arm and rushed him from the bedroom.

"Go away!" she had said, beginning to cry. "You can't *do* anything!..."

His adult eyes were damp when he awakened in his tiny room in the Monitor Corps base on Goglesk, and not for the first time he wondered to what extent the death of that incredibly old and fragile and warmhearted old lady had affected his subsequent life. The grief and sense of loss had faded, but not the memory of his utter helplessness, and he had not wanted to feel that way ever again. In later life, when she had encountered disease and injury and impending death, there had always been something, sometimes quite a lot, that he could do. And until his arrival on Goglesk he had never felt as helpless as that again.

"Go away," Khone had said when Conway's misguided attempt to help had resulted in the near-devastation of a town, and had probably caused untold psychological damage as well. And "You can't *do* anything," the Lieutenant had said.

But he was no longer a frightened, grieving young boy. He refused to believe that there was nothing he could do.

He thought about the situation as he bathed, dressed, and converted the room into its daytime mode, but ended by feeling angry with himself and even more helpless. He was a medic, he told himself, not a Cultural Contact specialist. The majority of his contacts were with extraterrestrials who were immobilized by disease or injury or examination-room restraints, and when close physical contact and investigative procedures were taken for granted. But not so on Goglesk.

Wainright had warned him about the phobic individualism of the FOKTs, and he had seen it for himself. Yet he had allowed his Earth-human instincts and feelings to take over when he should have controlled them—at least until he had understood a little more about the situation.

And now the only being who could have helped him understand the problem, Khone, would not want to meet him again except, perhaps, to offer physical violence.

Maybe he could try with another Gogleskan in a different area, presupposing that Wainright agreed to Conway's borrowing the base's only flyer for a lengthy period, and that the FOKTs had no means of long-distance communication. Certainly there had been nothing detected on the radio frequencies, and no evidence of visual or audible signaling systems or of messages carried by intelligent or nonintelligent runners or flyers.

But was it likely, he was thinking when his communicator beeped suddenly, that a species which so fanatically avoided close contact would be interested in keeping in touch over long distances?

"Your room sensors say that you're up and moving around," Wainright said, laughing. "Are you mentally awake as well, Doctor?"

Conway did not feel like laughing at anything, and he hoped the well-meaning Lieutenant was not intent on cheering him up. Irritably, he said, "Yes."

"Khone is outside," Wainright said, as if he was having trouble believing his own words. "It says that an obligation exists to return our visit of yesterday, and to apologize for any mental or physical distress the incident may have caused us. Doctor, it particularly wants to talk to you."

Extraterrestrials, thought Conway, not for the first time, *are full of surprises*. This one might have some answers, as well. As he left the room his pace could never have been described as the confident, unhurried tread of a Senior Physician. It was more like a dead run.

Chapter 7

IN spite of the painfully slow and impersonal style of speech and the lengthy pauses between the sentences, it was obvious that Khone wanted to talk. What was more, it wanted to ask questions. But the questions were extraordinarily difficult for it to verbalize because they were of a kind which had never before been asked by a member of its species.

Conway knew of many member species of the Galactic Federation whose viewpoints and behavior patterns were utterly alien and even repugnant to an Earth-human, even to an Earth-human medic with wide extraterrestrial experience like himself. He could imagine the tremendous effort Khone was putting into trying to understand this frightful off-worlder who, among other peculiarities, thought nothing of actually *touching* another being for purposes other than mating and infant care. He had a lot of sympathy and patience for a being engaged in such a struggle.

During one of the seemingly endless pauses he had tried to move the conversation along by taking the blame for what had happened, but Khone dismissed the apology by saying that if the off-worlders had not precipitated the calamity then some Gogleskan combination of events would have done so. It gave details of the damage which had been done. This would be repaired and the ship rebuilt in time, but it would not be surprised if a similar disaster overtook them before the work was completed.

Every time a joining occurred they lost a little ground, were left with less of their technology—simple though it was by off-worlder standards—so that the minor advances they had been able to achieve were being slowly eroded away. It had always been thus, according to the stories which had been handed down from generation to generation and in the scraps of written history which had somehow survived their regular orgies of self-destruction.

"If any assistance can be given," Conway said in impersonal Gogleskan fashion, "whether it is in the form of information, advice, physical help, or mechanisms capable of furnishing such help, a simple request is all that is necessary for it to be made available."

"The wish," Khone said slowly, "is that this burden be lifted from our race. The initial request is for information."

If yesterday's events could be so graciously forgiven, surely Khone would not be too bothered by Conway omitting the cumbersome verbal niceties which were a part of the barrier between them. He said, "You may ask any question on any subject without fear of offending me."

Khone's hair twitched at being addressed directly, but the healer's reply was immediate. "Information is requested regarding other off-world species of your experience who have similar problems as those encountered on Goglesk. Particular interest is felt in those species who have solved them."

The healer, too, had become slightly less impersonal in its mode of speech. Conway marveled at the effort it must have cost the other to break, or at least bend a little, its lifelong conditioning. The trouble was that he did not have the information required.

To give himself time to think, Conway did not reply directly, but began by describing some of the more exotic life-forms who made up the Federation—but not as he had described them earlier. Now he drew on his hospital experience to describe them as patients undergoing surgical or nonsurgical treatments for an incredible variety of diseases. He was trying to give Khone hope, but he knew that he was doing little more than stalling by describing clinical pictures and procedures to a being, albeit a doctor of sorts, who could not even touch its patients. Conway had never believed in misinforming his patients, by word or deed or omission, and he did not want to do so to another medic.

". . . However," he went on, "to my own certain knowledge the problem afflicting your species is unique. If a similar case had been encountered, it would have been thoroughly investigated and discussed in the literature and be required reading for the staff of a multispecies hospital.

"I am sorry," he continued, "but the only helpful suggestion I can make is that the condition be studied as closely as possible by me, with the cooperation of an entity who is both a patient and a doctor, you."

As he waited for Khone's reaction, Conway heard Wainright moving behind him, but the Lieutenant did not speak.

"Cooperation is possible, and desirable," the Gogleskan said finally, "but not close cooperation."

Conway gave a relieved sigh. "The structure behind me contains a compartment designed for the confinement and study of local fauna under conditions of minimum physical restraint. For the protection of observers, the compartment is divided by an invisible but extremely hard wall. Would a close approach for purposes of physical examination be possible in those conditions?"

"Provided the strength of the invisible wall is demonstrated," the Gogleskan said cautiously, "a close approach is possible."

Wainright cleared his throat and said, "Sorry, Doctor. Until now there has been no need to use that room and I've been storing fuel cells in it. Give me twenty minutes to tidy up."

While Khone and Conway walked slowly around to the rear of the building, he explained that the compartment had, as the healer could see, an external opening which allowed confined life-forms to return to their own environment quickly after release. No restraints whatsoever would be placed on Khone, Conway reassured the other, and it could break off any discussion or examination at will.

His intention was to try to find some explanation for the Gogleskan behavior by a close study of the physiology of the species, with particular emphasis on the cranial area, which displayed features completely new to Conway and which, for this reason, might suggest a line of investigation. But it was not his intention to cause physical or mental distress.

"Some discomfort is expected," the FOKT said.

To further reassure Khone, Conway entered the compartment first, and while the Gogleskan watched from the external entrance, he demonstrated with his fists and feet the strength of the transparent wall. Indicating the ceiling, he briefly described the purpose of the two-way communicator and the projectors of the nonmaterial restraining and manipulation devices, which would be used only with Khone's express permission. Then he went through the small door, outlined in white for visibility in that totally invisible wall, and left the FOKT to get used to the place.

Wainright had already moved the fuel cells from the observer's half of the compartment, and had replaced them with a tri-di projector, recordings made the previous day as well as basic information tapes of the type used during other-species first contacts, and all of Conway's medical equipment.

"I'll monitor and record from the comm center next door," Wainright said, pausing for a moment in the internal entrance. "Khone has already seen the information tapes, but I thought you might want to rerun the five-minute sequence on Sector General. If you need anything else, Doctor, let me know."

They were left alone in the compartment, separated only by a thin, transparent wall and about three meters of distance, which was much too far.

Conway placed the palm of one hand against the transparent surface at waist level, and said, "Please approach as closely as possible and try to place a manipulatory appendage on the other side of the transparent wall occupied by mine. There is no urgency. The purpose is to accustom you to close proximity to me without actual physical contact..."

He went on talking reassuringly as Khone came closer and, after several attempts and withdrawals, placed its cluster of digits opposite Conway's hand. They were now separated by less than half an inch. Slowly he used his other hand to bring out his scanner and place that, too, against the wall on a level with the FOKT's cranium. Without being asked, the Gogleskan pressed the side of its head section against the invisible surface.

"Excellent!" Conway said, refocusing his scanner. He went on. "While there are elements of the Gogleskan physiology which are completely strange to me, as a whole the life-form is similar to many warm-blooded oxygen-breathing species. The differences are centered in the cranial area, and it is this which requires examination and an explanation which might not have a purely physical basis.

"In short," he went on, "we are examining a fairly normal life-form that occasionally behaves abnormally. Now, if we accept that behavior patterns are established by environmental and evolutionary factors, we should begin by examining your past."

He gave Khone a moment to think, then continued.

"Lieutenant Wainright, who admits to being a fairly good amateur archeologist, tells me that your world has been remarkably stable since the time your presapient ancestors evolved. There have been no orbital changes, no major seismic disturbances, no ice ages or any marked alterations in the climatology. All of which indicates that your particular behavior pattern, the one which is presently hampering your progress as a culture, was evolved in response to a very early threat from natural enemies. What are, or were, these enemies?"

"We have no natural enemies," Khone replied promptly. "There is nothing on Goglesk which threatens us except ourselves."

Conway had trouble believing that. He moved his scanner to one of the areas where a sting lay partially hidden by cranial hair and then followed its connections to the poison sac while an enlarged picture of the process was projected onto the screen for Khone's benefit. He said, "That is a potent natural weapon whether it was used for attack or defense, and it would not have evolved without reason. Are there any memories, any written or spoken history, any fossil remains of a life-form so ferocious that it caused such a deadly defense to evolve?"

The answer was again no, but Conway had to ask the help of Wainright to explain fossils to the Gogleskan. It transpired that Khone had seen fossil remains from time to time but had not realized what they were or considered them of any importance. As a science archeology was unknown to its people. But now that Khone knew what the odd-shaped marks and objects in certain rocks signified, it seemed likely that the healer would father a new science.

"Have you experienced any dreams or nightmares about such a beast?" Conway asked, without looking up from his scanner.

"Only the phantasms of childhood," Khone said quickly, giving Conway the impression that it wanted to change the subject. "They rarely trouble adult minds."

"But when you do dream about them," Conway persisted, "is it possible to remember and describe this creature or creatures?"

Almost a full minute passed before the Gogleskan replied, and during that time Conway's scanner showed a perceptible bunching of the muscles surrounding the poison sac and at the base of the stings. Plainly he was moving into a very sensitive area. This answer, he thought, was going to be an important one.

But when it came the answer was disappointing, and seemed to invite only more questions.

"It is not a creature with a definite physical form," the FOKT said. "In the dreams there is a feeling of great danger, a formless threat from a fast-moving, ferocious entity which bites and tears and engulfs. It is a phantasm which frightens the young, and the thought of it distresses adults. The young may give way to their fears and join together for mutual comfort, because they lack the physical strength to inflict major damage to their surroundings. But adults must avoid such mental bad habits and remain mentally and physically apart."

Baffled, Conway said, "Are you telling me that young Gogleskans may link together at will, but not the adults?"

"It is difficult to stop them doing so," the FOKT replied. "But it is discouraged lest a habit develops which would be too difficult to break in adulthood. And while I realize that you are anxious to study the joining process without subjecting our artifacts to damage, to closely observe a joining between children without causing mental distress in the parents concerned, followed by an involuntary adult joining, would be impossible."

Conway sighed. Khone was way ahead of him, because that would have been his next request. Instead, he said, "Does my race in any way resemble this phantasm of your youth?"

"No," Khone replied. "But your close approach of yesterday, and in particular your physical contact with a Gogleskan, appeared to be a threat. The reaction and emission of the distress call was instinctive, not logical."

Helplessly, Conway said, "If we knew exactly what was responsible for what is clearly a species-wide panic reaction, we could try to negate it. But what *is* this bogeyman of yours?"

The lengthy silence which followed was broken by Wainright clearing his throat. Hesitantly, he said, "Considering the vague description, the speed and silence of its approach, and the fact that it rends and engulfs its prey, could it have been a large, airborne predator?"

Conway thought about that while he charted the nerve connections between the thin, shining tendrils lying in the coarser hair and the small, mineral-rich lobe at the center of the brain where they originated. He said, "Is there fossil evidence for such a creature? And isn't it possible, if this memory goes back to presapient times to the period when the FOKTs were sea-dwellers, that the predator was a swimmer rather than a flyer?"

The communicator was silent for a moment; then Wainright said, "I found no evidence of large avians on the few sites I examined, Doctor. But if we are going really far back to the time when all Gogleskan life was in the oceans, then some of it was very large indeed. There is an area of seabed which was thrown up fairly recently, in geological terms, about twenty miles south of here. I deep-probed a fossil-rich section which was once a deep subsea valley, meaning to work up a computer reconstruction whenever I had a few hours to spare. It made a very confusing picture, because a large number of the fossil remains are damaged or incomplete."

"Distortion due to seismic activity, do you think?" Conway asked.

"It's possible," the Lieutenant said doubtfully. "But my guess would be that it was inflicted by a contemporary agency. But the tape is in my room, Doctor. Shall I fetch it and see if the pictures, confusing as they are to me, jog our friend's racial memory?"

"Yes, please," Conway said. To Khone he went on. "If the recollection is not too distressing, can you tell me the number of times you have joined with other adults in response to a real or imagined threat? And can you describe the physical, mental, and emotional stages before, during, and subsequent to a joining? I do not wish to cause you pain, but it is important that this process be studied and understood if an answer to the problem is to be found."

It was obvious that the recollection was causing discomfort to Khone, and equally plain that the healer was going to cooperate to the best of its ability. Before yesterday, it told Conway, there had been three previous joinings. The sequence of events was, firstly, the accident or sudden surprise or physical threat which caused the being endangered to emit an audible distress signal which drew all of its fellows within hearing to it as well as placing them in the same emotional state. If one being was threatened then everyone within audible range was threatened and was under the same compulsion to react, to join and overcome the threat. Khone indicated the organ which produced the signal, a membrane which could be made to vibrate independent of the respiratory system.

The thought occurred to Conway that the membrane would have been even more effective under water, but he was too busy listening to interrupt.

Khone went on to describe the sense of increased safety as the body hair of the beings wove them together, and the pleasant, exciting feeling of increased intellect and awareness as the first few Gogleskans joined and shared minds. But that feeling died as more and more beings linked up and mentation became progressively more difficult and confused until it was submerged by the one, overwhelming need to protect the group by attacking anything and everything in the vicinity. Coherent thought at the individual level was impossible.

"... When the threat has been neutralized," Khone went on, "or the incident which initiated the fusion is over and even to the dim understanding of the group-entity no longer poses a threat, the group slowly breaks up. For a time the individuals feel mentally confused, physically tired, and ashamed of themselves and of the destruction they have caused. To survive as an intelligent race, every Gogleskan must strive to be a lonely person."

Conway did not reply. His mind was still trying to adjust to the sudden realization that the Gogleskans had telepathy.

Chapter 8

THE telepathic faculty had limitations, because the distress signal which triggered the joining was an audible rather than a mental one. It had to be telepathy by touch, then. He thought of the fine tendrils concealed by the coarse cranial hair. There were eight of them, which was more than enough to make contact with those of the beings pressed tightly around during a linkup.

He must have been thinking aloud, because Khone announced very firmly that such contact with another Gogleskan was acutely painful, and that the tendrils lay alongside those of the other group members but did not touch. Apparently the tendrils were organic transmitting and receiving antennae which operated by simple induction.

But the problem with telepathic races—and there were several of them in the Galactic Federation—was that the faculty worked only between members of the same species; with other races whose telepathic equipment operated on different frequencies or who did not possess the faculty, it worked rarely if at all. Conway had had a few experiences with projective telepaths—it was thought that Earth-humans had a latent ability but had evolved away from it—and the images he had received had been of short duration and accompanied by prior mental discomfort. It was also thought that races possessing a spoken and written language rather than a mental one tended to progress further and faster in the physical sciences.

The Gogleskans possessed both, and for some reason had been stopped dead in their cultural tracks.

"Is it agreed," Conway asked, very impersonally and

carefully because he was about to suggest something unpleasant, "that it is the instinctive linkup, when there is no longer a major threat to make it necessary, which is the basis of your problem? Is it further agreed that the tendrils, which are almost certainly the mechanism which initiates and maintains the group as a single entity, require close and detailed study if the problem is to be solved? However, a visual examination is not sufficient, and tests requiring direct contact would be necessary. These would include nerve conductivity measurements, the withdrawal of minute tissue samples for analysis, the introduction of external stimuli to ascertain if... Khone! None of these tests are painful!"

In spite of his hasty reassurance the Gogleskan was displaying signs of growing panic.

"I know that the thought of any kind of physical contact is distressing," Conway went on quickly as he thought of a new approach, beautiful in its simplicity provided the personal dangers were ignored, "because there is an instinctive reaction to anyone or anything which might be a threat. But if it were demonstrated, on the instinctive as well as the cerebral level, that I am not a threat, then it might be possible for you to overcome this instinctive reaction.

"What I propose is this..."

Wainright returned while he was talking. The Lieutenant stood listening, the tape gripped tightly in his hand, until Conway had finished. Then he said in a frightened voice, "Doctor, you're mad."

It took a much longer time to obtain the Lieutenant's agreement than to get Khone's, but finally Conway had his way. Wainright drew a litter from stores and the Doctor was placed on it and securely restrained with straps around the feet, legs, arms and body—the restraints had a quick-release capability which could be remotely operated by the Lieutenant; Wainright had insisted on that—and he was moved into Khone's half of the observation compartment. The litter was set at a comfortable height for the Gogleskan healer to work, if it was able.

The idea was that if he could not physically examine

Khone then the Gogleskan would examine Conway, while he was utterly helpless and incapable of any threatening behavior. It would accustom the healer to the idea of physical examination and investigation against the time when it would be Conway's turn. But that time, it soon became obvious, would be long delayed.

Khone approached him closely without too much distress and, under Conway's direction, used the scanner with a fair degree of skill. But it was the instrument which touched him, not Khone itself. Conway remained absolutely still on the litter, moving only his eyes to watch Khone's hesitant movements, or the Lieutenant, who was projecting his tape onto the big screen.

Suddenly he felt a touch, so light that it might have been a feather falling onto the back of his hand and then sliding off again. Then the touch was repeated, more firmly this time.

He tried not to move even his eyes lest Khone shy away, so he was aware from his peripheral vision of an expanse of stiff, Gogleskan hair and three of Khone's manipulators, two of which were holding the scanner, moving along the side of his head. He felt another light touch in the area of the temporal artery; then very gently, the tip of a manipulator began exploring the convolutions of his ear.

Abruptly Khone withdrew, its membrane vibrating softly in muted distress.

Conway thought of the strength of the conditioning Khone had been fighting just to touch him the first time, and he felt an admiration for the dumpy little creature so great, and concern for its species as a whole so intense, that he found it difficult to speak for a few minutes.

"Apologies for the mental distress," Conway said finally, "but it should lessen as the contacts are repeated. But audible distress signals are being generated even though you know that I have neither the wish nor the ability to endanger you. With your agreement the external door of this compartment should be closed lest members of your species within audible range think that you are being threatened and come to join with you."

"There is understanding," Khone said without hesitation, "and agreement."

On the big screen the Lieutenant was playing back the tape which showed the dense mass of fossilized remains revealed by his deep probes, rotating the viewpoint and overlaying a scale grid so that a true idea of the shapes and sizes could be shown. Khone paid little attention to the display because, Conway realized, a species with such a primitive level of technology would not immediately comprehend the solid reality represented by a few thin lines on a dark screen. It was much more interested in the three-dimensional reality of the Doctor and it was approaching him again.

Conway, however, was intensely interested in the images on the screen.

He kept his eyes on it while two of Khone's manipulators gently parted the hair on his scalp. To the Lieutenant, he said, "Those incomplete fossils look as if they have been torn apart, and I wouldn't mind betting that if you ask that computer to reconstruct one of them using the data available from the Khone physiological material, you will have a recognizable presapient FOKT. But what is that... that overgrown vegetable hanging in the middle of them?"

Wainright laughed. "I was hoping you would tell me, Doctor. It looks like a deformed, stemless rose, with spikes or teeth growing from the edges of some of the petals, and it's *big*."

"The shape doesn't make sense," Conway said quietly as the Gogleskan shifted its attention to one of his hands. "As a mobile sea-dweller it should have fins rather than limbs, but there is no sign of streamlining along its direction of motion, or even a basic symmetry about its center of..."

He broke off to answer a question from Khone regarding the hair on his wrist, and he took the opportunity of weakening the other's conditioning a little more by suggesting that it perform a simple surgical procedure on him. It would involve removing a small area of hair, and using a fine needle in conjunction with the scanner to withdraw a small quantity of blood from a minor vein at the back of Conway's hand. He assured Khone that the procedure would be painless and no harm would be done even if the needle were not positioned with complete accuracy.

He explained that it was the kind of test which was done countless times every day at Sector General on a wide variety of patients, and later analysis of the sample taken revealed a great deal about the condition of these patients, and in many cases, the data obtained was instrumental in curing them.

There would be very little direct physical contact involved in taking the sample, because Khone would be using the scanner, swab, scissors, and a hypodermic, he added encouragingly. Just as there would be minimal body contact if or when Conway performed similar tests on the Gogleskan.

For a moment Conway thought that he had rushed things too much, because Khone had backed away until it was pressing against the inside of the closed external door. It remained there, its hair twitching while it fought another battle with its conditioning, then it slowly returned to the litter. While he waited for it to speak, Conway took a quick look at the amazingly lifelike picture which was taking form on Wainright's screen.

The Lieutenant had incorporated in the display all of the FOKT data as well as information he had gleaned earlier on the subsea vegetation of prehistoric times. The fossil remains, which the computer had reconstructed as slightly smaller versions of present-day Gogleskans, lay singly and in small, linked groups among the gently waving marine vegetation, lit by bright, greenish yellow sunlight which filtered down from the wave-wrinkled surface above. Only in the enormous, roselike object which lay in the center of the picture was there a lack of detail. An idea about it began to take shape at the back of Conway's mind, but Khone spoke suddenly before it could form.

The Gogleskan was still not taking any interest in the screen.

"If this test were to cause pain," Khone asked, "what would be the procedure then? And would it be preferable, in the present circumstances, for the blood sample to be taken by and from oneself?"

A helpful but cautious entity, this Khone, Conway thought, trying not to laugh. He said, "If a procedure is expected to cause discomfort, a quantity of the material contained in one of the phials colored in yellow and black diagonal bands is withdrawn and injected into the site. The quantity required is dependent on the period and degree of discomfort which one is expecting to cause.

"The material concerned is a painkiller for my species," he went on, "as well as a muscle relaxant. But it is not required in this instance..."

While he continued to give the directions for withdrawing the blood sample, he told Khone that it was much easier to perform such work on a subject other than oneself. He did not, at that time, make any mention of the fact that if he was to obtain a specimen of FOKT blood from Khone, the first thing he would have wanted to discover was if the yellow and black marked medication, or one of the other similar preparations in his supply, was suited to the Gogleskan metabolism. If one of them was suitable and there was an opportunity of injecting it, Khone would be left in such a pain-free, relaxed, and massively tranquilized state that subsequent and more revealing tests would have been no problem at all.

A muscle relaxed, he thought, his eyes going back to Wainright's display, *as opposed to a muscle in spasm*!...

The large object centering the screen lacked the symmetry and structural repetition of a vegetable—it looked like a sheet of paper which had been crushed and twisted into a loose ball. But if that idea was correct, the predator must have pulled itself into that shape. Conway shivered in spite of himself.

That Gogleskan venom was potent stuff.

To Wainright, he said quickly, "How does this sound? The FOKT fossils were those beings who did not survive the initial attack of the creature, and some of them are linked, indicating that they were part of a larger group. This FOKT group-entity attacked or defended itself against the predator with its stings, all of them. The quantity of venom injected must have sent the beastie into multiple muscular spasm, and it must have literally tied itself into a knot as it died. Can you get your computer to unravel that knot?"

Wainright nodded, and soon the twisted, convoluted shape at the center of the screen was surrounded by a fainter image of itself which was slowly unfolding. This had to be the answer for that weird shape, Conway thought, because nothing else made sense. Occasionally he asked for expanded views of the enormous fossil's skeletal structure, and each one supported his theory. But the Lieutenant was forced to reduce the size several times as the ghostly, unfolding image overran the edges of the screen.

"It's beginning to look like a bird," Wainright said. "Parts of the wing are very fragile. In fact, it seems to be *all* wing."

"That's because the fossil remains are of the skeleton and skin only," Conway replied. "There must have been almost total wastage of muscle and soft tissue which was attached to that bone structure. In the areas where you are indicating the wing... Now you've got me thinking of it as a bird... The wing thickness should be increased by a factor of five or six. But with that bone structure the wing could not have been rigid. I'd say that it undulated rapidly rather than flapping, and propelled the beastie forward at great speed. And that lateral split in the wing inboard leading edges is interesting. It reminds me of the engine intakes of the old jet aircraft, except that these intakes have teeth..."

He broke off because Khone was jabbing hesitantly at the back of his hand with the hypo. For the first time Conway understood what a patient had to go through at the hands of a trainee medical technician.

"The jointing at the base of the wings," he went on when the Gogleskan had found the proper vein, "suggests that the mouths on the wing leading edges opened and closed as it swam, eating everything that got in its way and passing the food through two alimentary canals to the stomach housed in that cylindrical bulge along the center line. The tegument was thicker along the leading edges, and probably sting-proof, and the stomach was probably capable of dealing with the FOKT venom even though it is lethal when injected through softer areas of tegument into the bloodstream.

"The only defense the FOKTs could offer was to link up and present themselves as a solid wall in its path," he continued excitedly. "Quite a few of them would die before the group entity folded around the predator and stung it to death. The incomplete fossil remains indicate that. But I hate to think of what it must have been like for the group-members as a whole while they were mentally linked to their dying friends . . ."

He cringed inwardly as he thought of how they all must have suffered, and died, every time one of their group did so. And they would have done so many times if the predator's attacks were a regular occurrence. What was worse, prior to an attack they all knew what was ahead of them through the minds of previous survivors—all the fear and pain and multiple dying by proxy.

At last he understood the severity of the racial psychosis which gripped the whole Gogleskan species. As individuals they feared and hated a joining, or any close physical or mental contact or cooperation which might lead to the possibility of a linkup. Subconciously to join was to suffer remembered pain, pain which could only be assuaged by a blind, berserker rage which in turn blotted out the capacity to think or to control their actions. Their fear of that particular species of predator must have been extreme, and even though their old enemy was extinct or was still a sea-dweller, they had not been able to forget it or develop a less self-defeating method of self-defense.

The main trouble was that the defense mechanism was so hypersensitive, even after the enlapsed millennia since it was needed, that it could be triggerred by an imagined or potential threat as well as an actual one.

Khone had finally completed withdrawing the blood sample. The back of Conway's hand felt like a pincushion, but he said highly complimentary things about the FOKT healer's first off-planet surgical procedure, and meant every word of them. While the other was carefully transferring the contents of the syringe into a sterile phial, he returned his attention to the screen.

The creature was completely unfolded now, and the Lieutenant had reduced the image again so that it would fit within the limits of the screen. Wainright had also added all the available data and theory on coloration, probable method of locomotion, and the wing-synchronized mouth and teeth movements. It moved slowly in the center of the big screen, a vast, dark gray, dreadful shape more than eighty meters across, undulating and flapping ponderously like an enormous, Earthly stingray, sucking in, tearing apart, and eating everything in its path.

This was the Gogleskan nightmare from their prehistoric past, and the figures of the reconstructed FOKT fossils were tiny blobs of color near the lower edge of the screen.

"Wainright!" Conway said urgently. "*Kill that picture!...*"

But he was too late. Khone, its work completed, had turned to look at the screen—and was confronted with the three-dimensional picture of a moving and seemingly living creature which up until then had inhabited only its subconscious. In the confined space of the compartment its distress call was deafening.

Conway cursed his own stupidity as the panic-stricken Gogleskan stumbled about the floor within a few feet of his litter. Khone had shown little interest in the display when it had been a collection of fine lines, since it lacked the experience to appreciate the three-dimensional reality which they represented. But the Lieutenant's final picture was much too realistic for any Gogleskan to view and remain wholly sane.

He saw the FOKTs dumpy body come toward him, then lurch past. Its multicolor hair was standing on end and twitching, its four stings were fully extended, dropletes of venom oozing from the tips, but the sound coming from its membranes seemed fractionally less deafening. Conway lay rigid, not even swiveling his eyes as the being moved away and then came back again.

The reduction in the volume of its distress call made

it obvious that Khone was fighting its conditioning and Conway had to help it in the only way possible, by remaining absolutely motionless. Out of the corner of his eye he saw the Gogleskan stop, one of its stings only inches away from the side of his face and the stiff, bristling hair touching his coveralls. He could feel its breath puffing gently across his forehead and smell the faint, peppermint smell which seemed to be its body odor. Khone was trembling, whether with fear at the Lieutenant's display or in indecision over whether or not to attack, Conway did not know.

If he stayed absolutely still, he told himself desperately, he should not represent a threat. If he moved, however, he knew with a dreadful certainty that the Gogleskan would sting him, instinctively, without thinking. But there was another aspect of the FOKT behavior pattern which he had forgotten.

They blindly attacked enemies, but any being who was not a threat and had managed to remain in such close physical proximity as Conway had done had to be a friend.

At times like this, friends linked up.

Conway was suddenly aware of the stiff bristles scratching against his clothing and trying to weave themselves into the fabric of his coveralls in the area of his neck and shoulder. The sting was still too close to the side of his face for comfort, but somehow it seemed to be less threatening. He held absolutely still, anyway. Then he saw, clearly because it was moving just two inches above his eyes, one of the long, fine tendrils. He felt it fall, featherlight, across his forehead.

A Gogleskan joining was mental as well as physical, Conway knew, but he did not foresee any more success for the telpathic linkup than for the physical one.

He was wrong.

It began as a deep, unlocalized itch inside his skull, and if his hands and arms had not been immobilized he would have been poking desperately at his ears with his fingers. He was aware, too, of a maddening confusion of sounds, pictures, and feelings which were not his own. He had experienced the same sensation many times, after taking extraterrestrial physiology tapes at the hospital, but on those occasions the alien impressions had been coherent and orderly. He felt now as if he were watching a tri-di show with sensory augmentation when the channel selector control was malfunctioning. The bright but chaotic images and impressions became more intense, and he wanted to close his eyes in the hope that they would go away, but he dared not even blink.

Suddenly the picture held steady and the feelings were sharp and clear, and for a few seconds Conway knew what it was like to be the intensely lonely and intellectually frustrated entity that was an adult Gogleskan. The breadth of intelligence and sensitivity of Khone's mind awed him, and he was aware of the many ways in which the Gogleskan healer had used that mind, long before the Monitor Corps or Conway had arrived on Goglesk, to fight and circumvent the mind-destroying conditioning which their evolution had imposed on them.

He was sure, because he was in Khone's mind and the healer was sure, that its mind was nothing extraordinary so far as FOKT mental capacity was concerned. But their high intelligence could not be shared except by the slow, impersonal, and imprecise spoken language, and a true meeting of minds was possible only during the brief period between the initial linkup and the coarsening and confusion of intellect which immediately followed it. His admiration for this individual member of a race of intensely reluctant individualists was great indeed.

There is no coarsening or loss of definition in the thoughts we are exchanging.

The words which appeared in Conway's mind were overlaid by feelings of pleasure, gratitude, curiosity... and hope.

The process of establishing the mental linkup between your people must trigger an area of your endocrine system which desensitizes the entire cerebral process, probably to reduce the pain which was suffered in prehistoric times following a linkup and during the predator attack. But I am not a Gogleskan, so the desensitizing mechanism is absent. However, a precise study of the endocrinology involved should be undertaken without delay and the gland isolated, and if surgical intervention is indicated...

Too late he realized where that line of thought was taking him and the wide—and to Khone frightening—surgical associations it opened up. With a tremendous mental effort the Gogleskan had adapted to the close presence and physical contact with an off-worlder, and Conway *knew* precisely how much of an effort that had been. But now the healer was sharing Conway's mind, sharing his thoughts and feelings and experience of entities who staffed or were being cured at Sector General and who made the seagoing nightmare from Goglesk's past seem like a domestic pet by comparison.

Khone could not take it, and its distress signal, which had grown quieter over the past few minutes, roared out again at full, frantic intensity. But the little being was maintaining contact in spite of the alien nightmare its thought tendril was receiving, and Conway was suffering with it.

He tried to think reassuring thoughts, tried to make the Gogleskan's mind as well as his own change the mental subject. He had blinked several times but had otherwise remained still, and he thought, or rather he hoped, that Khone would continue to treat him as an immobile and helpless nonthreat. But was it his imagination or had Khone's appearance changed suddenly?

The stiff, multicolor hair was more clearly defined and the nearest sting had developed new highlights. For a moment his fear became even greater than Khone's as he realized what was happening.

"No, don't!..." he began, as loudly as he could without moving his lips. But the Gogleskan membrane was vibrating too loudly for Wainright to hear him.

"I've opened the outer door, Doctor," the Lieutenant shouted, the communicator volume turned high so that he would be heard over the noise Khone was making. "I'm cutting your restraints, *now*. Get out of there!"

"I'm not in danger," Conway called, but his voice was drowned out by that earsplitting distress signal and the overamplified Wainright. And he was lying anyway, because when the straps dropped away he was in terrible danger.

He was potentially mobile again, no longer helpless, and had therefore become a threat.

In the instant before the tendril was withdrawn Conway knew that Khone did not want to sting him, but that made no difference at all to what was a purely reflex action. As he rolled desperately onto the floor, he felt the jab of the blunt point of the sting thudding into his shoulder. One of his ankles was entangled in the foot restraints as he tried to crawl away, and another jab tore his coveralls and scratched his thigh. Again he tried to crawl toward the outer entrance, but first his arm and then his leg doubled up in muscular spasm, and he toppled onto his side, unable to move and facing the transparent partition. The two affected limbs seemed to be on fire.

The muscles in his neck and in the area of the scapula were knotting in cramp, and the fire was spreading from the hip puncture to the abdominal muscles. He wondered if the venom would affect the involuntary muscle systems as well, specifically those operating his heart and lungs. If it did then he had not long to live. The pain was so intense that the thought did not frighten him as badly as it should have. Desperately he tried to think of something he should do before he passed out.

"Wainright..." he began weakly.

Khone's distress call had reduced in volume, and the healer had not tried to sting him again—obviously he was no longer a threat. The Gogleskan stood a few feet from him, its hair agitated by its stings lying flat against its head, looking like a harmless multicolored haystack. He tried again.

"Wainright," he said slowly and painfully. "The yellow and black phial. Inject all of it..."

But the Lieutenant was not at the other side of the partition, and the connecting door was still closed. Maybe Wainright intended coming around to the external door to drag Conway out, but he could not move himself around to see. It was becoming difficult to see anything.

Before he passed out, Conway was aware of regular fluctuations in the lighting which reminded him of something. A heavy power drain, he thought weakly, of the kind required to punch a signal through hyperspace...

Chapter 9

HE seemed to be attached to every sensor and monitoring device in the unit, Conway thought as he looked up at the displays from the unfamiliar viewpoint of a patient, and luxuriated in the feeling of his limbs stretched to full extension and free of the excruciating cramp. He moved his eyes to see Prilicla regarding him from its position on the ceiling and the figures of Murchison and Naydrad at one side of his bed, also looking down at him. Between them was a large eye supported by a long tubular appendage which had been extruded by Danalta with the same purpose in mind. Conway moistened his lips.

"What happened?" he said.

"That," Murchison said, "is supposed to be the second question. The first is 'Where am I?'"

"I know where I am, dammit. On the casualty deck of *Rhabwar*. And why am I still wired up to that thing? Surely you can see that the biosensors are indicating optimum levels on all vital functions. What I want to know is how I got here."

The pathologist breathed gently through her nose. "Mentation and memory seem unimpaired, and you are your usual short-tempered self. But you must rest. The Gogleskan venom has been neutralized, and in spite of what the displays are showing, there is marked physical debility and the likelihood of delayed shock as a result of severe mental trauma. Massive rest is indicated, at least until we return to the hospital and you are given a thorough checkout.

"And don't think you can pull your Senior Physician's rank on me to get up," she said sweetly as Conway opened his mouth to do just that. "In this instance you are the patient and not the doctor, Doctor."

"This is a good time," Prilicla broke in at that moment, "for us to withdraw and so enable you to get the rest you require, friend Conway. We are all feeling pleased and relieved that you are recovering, and I think it would be less exhausting for you if we left and allowed friend Murchison to answer your questions."

Prilicla scuttled across the ceiling toward the entrance, Naydrad growled something which did not translate and followed the empath, and Danalta withdrew its eye support limb, stabilized as a dark green, lumpy ball, and rolled after them. Murchison began removing the unnecessary biosensors and switching off the monitors, silently and with more concentration than the work warranted.

"What *did* happen?" he asked quietly. When there was no response he went on. "That venom, I was trying to tie myself into knots. I wanted Wainright to inject the muscle relaxant, but he wasn't there. Then I seem to remember the lights dimming, and I knew he was using the hyperspace radio. But I didn't expect to wake up on *Rhabwar*..."

Or wake up ever again, he finished silently.

Still without looking at him she explained that the ambulance ship had been testing new equipment just beyond the Jump distance from Sector General, and with the full medical team on board. Because they knew the exact coordinates of Goglesk when the Lieutenant's hypersignal came in, they were able to emerge close to the planet, with their lander ready to launch, and they had been able to reach him in just under four hours.

They had found him still trying to tie himself in knots, but the muscular spasm had been reduced significantly by a massive dose of the relaxant DM82, so the knots were loose enough for him not to have broken any bones or torn any muscles or tendons. He had been very lucky.

Conway nodded and said seriously, "So the Lieutenant was able to get to me with the muscle relaxant in time. I'd say with seconds to spare."

Murchison shook her head. "It was the native Gogleskan, Khone, who administered the DM82. After damn well nearly killing you, it saves your life! It kept asking if you would be all right when we were taking you away, shouting at us until the entry port was sealed. You make some peculiar friends, Doctor."

"It had to make a tremendous mental effort to give me that shot," Conway said, "a bigger effort, perhaps, than I could have made in similar circumstances. How close did it come while you were transferring me to the lander?"

Murchison thought for a moment, then said, "When Lieutenant Haslam, who was piloting, and I met Wainright at the lock, it came to within twenty meters. When Naydrad, Prilicla, and Danalta came out with the litter, it became nervous and moved back to about twice that distance. Wainright told us what had happened between it and you, but we did not act or say anything which could be construed as hostile even though, personally, I would have liked to give it a quick kick in whatever it uses as a *gluteus maximus* for what it did to you. Maybe it simply feared retribution."

"Knowing its feelings as I do," Conway said seriously, "I think it would have welcomed retribution."

Murchison breathed through her nose once again and sat down on the edge of the litter, twisting around so as to face him and placing her hands on the pillow beside his shoulders. Her face lost its cool, clinical expression and she said shakily, "Damn you, Doctor, you nearly got yourself killed."

Suddenly her arms were around him and her face was close to his. Conway moved his head away quickly, without thinking. She straightened up, looking surprised.

"I'm . . . I'm not feeling like myself today," he said. Again without thinking he had used the stock phrase which, at Sector General, was the acceptable excuse for strange or uncharacteristic behavior.

"You mean," she said furiously, "that you've an

Educator tape riding you, and O'Mara sent you to Goglesk without erasing it? What are you carrying, a Tralthan, a Melfan? I know both of those species consider the Earth-human female body to be something less than desirable. Or did you *volunteer* to take an Educator tape on vacation? Some vacation!"

Conway shook his head. "It isn't a physiology tape, and O'Mara had nothing to do with it. There was a very close, and quite intense, telepathic contact with Khone. It was unexpected, an accident, but the Gogleskan FOKT classification has some remarkable behavior characteristics which include..."

Before Conway could stop himself he was describing the whole Gogleskan situation and his experience with the town-wrecking group entity and with Khone as an individual. As one of the hospital's leading pathologists, second only to the great Thornnastor itself, her professional interst should have been aroused, and it would be, in time. But right then it was obvious that she was not thinking about anything except the state in which she had found Conway a few hours earlier.

"The important thing," she said, trying to smile, "is that you don't want anyone to come close to you, unless it looks like a multicolor haystack. As an excuse it certainly beats having a headache."

Conway smiled back. "Not at all. Bodily contact can be made without initiating a Joining, at any time, provided the intention is associated with reproduction." He reached up with one hand, and with the palm pressed gently against the back of her neck he pulled her face down toward his. "Would you like to rerun that last bit again?"

"You are severely debilitated," she said, looking relieved and trying to duck from under his hand—but not working very hard at it. Conway spread his fingers through her hair and did not let go even when their faces were only a few inches apart. She went on softly. "You're making an awful mess of my hair."

Conway slipped his other hand around her waist and said, "Don't worry. It makes you look much more like a desirable haystack..."

He had no discomfort and he did not feel particularly debilitated, but suddenly he began to shake as the delayed shock from the Khone incident hit him, and with it the memory of those excruciating muscle spasms and the knowledge of just how close to death he had been. She held him tightly until the shaking had stopped, and for a long time afterward.

They both knew that the gentle and understanding Prilicla, from its quarters two decks above them, was aware of the emotional radiation of every being in the ship. The telepath would ensure that nobody interrupted them until curative therapy was concluded.

It was ten hours later—*Rhabwar* had not needed to break any records on the return trip—that they locked on to the Casualty Admission Port on Level 103. Charge Nurse Naydrad, who could be fanatical at times about the regulations, insisted on bringing him into the observation ward on the litter. Conway was equally insistent about sliding back the canopy and sitting up during the transfer, to reassure the Earth-human and extraterrestrial colleagues who were waiting inside the entry port to inquire worriedly about his condition. Murchison had left him to make her report to Thornnastor, and Prilicla had gone on ahead to escape the somewhat turbulent emotional radiation being generated in the vicinity of Conway's litter.

But it took less than an hour in the observation ward for the Physician-in-Charge and its staff to complete their examination and agree with Conway's self-diagnosis that he was in all respects physically fit.

An hour later he was in the office of Major O'Mara, who was not overly concerned with things physical.

"This is not the usual Educator tape impression," the Chief Psychologist said when Conway had described his experiences with Khone. "Normally a tape contains the complete mind record of the being who donated it, and in spite of the psychological tricks which the recipient plays on himself or itself, the taped-in personality of that of the being receiving the tape is completely distinct. The recording is not subject to alteration. For this reason an erasure can be performed without any ill-effects on the recipient's personality or mental state. But you, Doctor, had a full, two-way exchange with this Khone character, which means that you have assimilated a fairly large body of memories, feelings, and thought processes into the Conway mind matrix and, God help its future sanity, Khone has been impressed with quite a lot of your material, and the minds of both parties were aware of and were modified by the process. For this reason I cannot see any way that we can selectively remove the Gogleskan material without the risk of personality damage. In psychological terms there has been feedback from both minds.

"There is a possibility, a small one," O'Mara went on gruffly, "that if Khone could be persuaded to come here and donate its own Educator tape for study, something could be tried which—"

"It wouldn't come," Conway said.

"Judging by what you've told me, I'm inclined to agree," the Chief Psychologist said, a tinge of sympathy creeping into his tone. "This means that you are stuck with your Gogleskan alter ego, Conway. Is it . . . bad?"

Conway shook his head. "It is no more alien than a Melfan tape, except that there are times when I'm not sure whether it is Khone or myself reacting to a given situation. I think I can handle it without psychiatric assistance."

"Good," O'Mara said drily, and added, "You're afraid the treatment might be worse than the condition, and you're probably right."

"It isn't good," Conway said firmly. "The Gogleskan business, I mean. Their whole species is being held back by what amounts to a racial conditioned reflex! We will have to do something about that berserker group-entity problem."

"*You* will have to do something about it," O'Mara said, "between a few other jobs we have lined up for you. After all, you are the Senior Physician with the most knowledge of the Gogleskan situation, so why should I assign anyone else? But first, I assume you found a little time between wrecking Gogleskan towns and being stung nearly to death by your FOKT colleague to decide whether or not you want to try for Diagnostician? And that you discussed some of the, er, ramifications with your personal pathologist?"

Conway nodded. "We've discussed it, and I'll give it a try. But these other jobs you mentioned, I'm not sure that I'm able to—"

The Chief Psychologist held up a hand. "Of course you are able. Both Senior Physician Prilicla and Pathologist Murchison have pronounced you in all respects psychologically and physically fit." He looked steadily at Conway's reddening face for a moment, then added, "She did not go into detail, just said that she was satisfied. You have another question?"

Warily, Conway asked,"How many other jobs?"

"Several," O'Mara replied. "They are detailed in the tape which you can pick up from the outer office. Oh, yes, Doctor, I expected you to decide as you have done. But now you will have to accept a greater measure of responsibility for your diagnoses, decisions, and treatment directives than you have been accustomed to as a Senior Physician, and for patients which only your subordinates will see unless something goes badly amiss. Naturally, you will be allowed to seek the help and advice of colleagues at Diagnostician or any other level, but only if you can satisfy me, and yourself, that you can no longer proceed without such assistance.

"Knowing you, Doctor," he added sourly, "it would be difficult to say which of us would be harder to satisfy on that point."

Conway nodded. It was not the first time that O'Mara had criticized him for being too professionally proud, or pigheaded. But he had been able to avoid serious trouble by also being right on most of the occasions. He cleared his throat.

"I understand," he said quietly. "But it still seems to me that the Gogleskan situation requires early attention."

"So does the problem in the FROB geriatric unit," O'Mara said. "Not to mention the urgent need to design accommodation for a pregnant Protector and its offspring, as well as sundry teaching duties, lectures in theater, and any odd jobs which may come up and for which your peculiar qualities suit you. Some of these problems have been with us for a long time, although not, of course, for as many thousands of years as those of your Gogleskan friends. As a would-be Diagnostician you also have the responsibility for deciding which case or cases should be given priority. After due consideration, of course."

Conway nodded. His vocal chords seemed to have severed communications with his brain while it tried to absorb all the implications of a multiple assignment the individual sections of which were just this side of impossible. He knew of some of those problems and the Diagnosticians who had worked on them, and the hospital grapevine had carried some bloodcurdling accounts of some of the failures. And now, for the period of assessment as acting Diagnostician, the problems were his.

"Don't sit there gaping at me," O'Mara said. "I'm sure you can find something else to do."

Chapter 10

It was an unusual meeting for Conway in that he was the only medic present—the others were exclusively Monitor Corps officers charged with the responsibilities for various aspects of hospital maintenance and supply, and Major Fletcher, the Captain of the *Rhabwar*. It was doubly unusual in that Conway, wearing his gold-edged acting Diagnostician's armband with a nonchalance he did not feel, was solely and completely himself.

There were no Educator tapes which could help him with this problem, only the experience of Major Fletcher and himself.

"The initial requirement," he began formally, "is for

accommodation, food supply, and treatment facilities for a gravid FSOJ life-form better known to some of us as one of the Protectors of the Unborn. It is an extremely dangerous being, nonintelligent in the adult stage, which on its home planet is continuously under attack from the time it is born until it dies, usually at the tentacles and teeth of its last-born. Captain, if you please..."

Fletcher tapped buttons on his console, and the briefing screen lit with the picture of an adult Protector taken during one of *Rhabwar*'s rescue missions, followed by material on other FSOJs collected on their home world. But it was the way that the Protector's snapping teeth and flailing tentacles warped and dented the ambulance ship's internal plating which caused the watchers to grunt in disbelief.

"As you can see," Conway resumed, "the FSOJ is a large, immensely strong, oxygen-breathing life-form with a slitted carapace from which protrude those four heavy tentacles and a tail and head. The tentacles and tail have large, osseous terminations resembling organic spiked clubs, and the principal features of the head are the recessed and heavily protected eyes, and the jaws. You will also note that the four stubby legs which project from the underside of the carapace possess bony spurs which make these limbs additional weapons of offense. On their planet of origin all of these weapons are needed.

"Their young remain in the womb until physical development is sufficiently advanced for them to survive birth into their incredibly savage environment, and during the embryo stage they are telepathic. But this aspect of the problem is not in your area.

"Constant and savage conflict is such a vital part of their lives," Conway went on, "that they sicken and die without it. For that reason the preparation of accommodation for this life-form will be much more difficult than any you have been asked to provide hitherto. The compartment will have to be structurally robust. Captain Fletcher, here, will be able to give you information on the beastie's physical strength and degree of mobility, and if he sounds as if he is exaggerating, believe me, he is not. The cargo chamber on *Rhabwar* had to be completely rebuilt after the FSOJ had been confined in it during an eleven-hour trip to the hospital."

"My tibia needed repairing, too," Fletcher said drily.

Before Conway could go on there was another interruption. Colonel Hardin, who was the hospital's Dietician-in-Chief, said, "I get the impression that your FSOJ fights and eats its food, Doctor. Now, you must be aware of the rule here that live food is never provided, only synthesized animal tissue or imported vegetation if the synthesizers can't handle it. Some of the food animals used in the Federation bear a close resemblance to other sentient Galactic citizens, many of whom find the eating of nonvegetable matter repugnant and—"

"No problem, Colonel," Conway broke in. "The FSOJ will eat anything. Your biggest headache will be the accommodation, which is going to resemble more closely a medieval torture chamber than a hospital ward."

"Are we to be given information regarding the purpose of this project?" asked an officer whom Conway had not seen before. He wore the yellow tabs of a maintenance specialist and the insignia of a major. He smiled as he went on. "It would help guide us in the initial design work, as well as satisfying our curiosity."

"The work is not secret," Conway replied, "and the only reason I would not like it to be discussed widely is that we may fall short of our expectations. This, considering the fact that I have been given charge of the project, could cause personal embarrassment, no more than that.

"Continuous conception takes place within every member of this species," he went on briskly, "and the intention is to closely study this process with the ultimate aim of inhibiting the effects of the mechanism which destroys the sentient and telepathic portion of the embryo's brain prior to its birth. If a newly born Protector retained its sentience and telepathic faculty, it could in time communicate with its own Unborn and, hopefully, establish a bond which would make it impossible for them to harm each other. We will also be trying to gradually reduce the violence of the environmental beating they take and stimulate, medically rather than physically, the release of the complex secretions which are triggered by this activity. That way they should gradually get out of the habit of trying to kill and eat everything they see. Also, the answers we find must enable the FSOJs to continue to survive on their frightful planet, and help them escape from the evolutionary trap which has rendered impossible any chance of the species' developing a civilized culture."

They have a lot in common with the Gogleskans, he thought. Smiling, he added, "But this is one of my problems. Another is making sure that you fully understand yours."

There followed a long and at times overheated discussion at the end of which they understood all of the problems—including the need for urgency. Their captive Protector could not be held indefinitely in the old Tralthan Observation Ward on Level 202 with a couple of FROB maintenance engineers taking turns at beating it with metal bars. The two Hudlars, despite their immense strength and fearsome aspect, were kindly souls, and the work—in spite of constant reassurances that the activity was necessary for the Protector's well-being—was causing them serious psychological discomfort.

Everybody had problems, Conway thought. But his own most immediate one, hunger, was easily solved.

He had timed his visit to the dining hall to coincide with the meal schedule of *Rhabwar*'s medical team, primarily to see Murchison, and he found Prilicla, Naydrad, and Danalta with her at a table designed for Melfan ELNTs. The pathologist did not speak until he had finished tapping out his food selection, an enormous steak with double the usual accessories.

"Obviously you are still yourself," she said, looking enviously at his plate, "or your alter egos are nonvegetarian. Synthetics are still fattening, you know. Why is it you don't grow an abdomen like a pregnant Crepellian?"

"It's my psychological approach to eating which is responsible," Conway said with a grin as he initiated major surgery on the steak. "Food is simply a fuel which has to be burned up. It must be obvious to you all that I am not enjoying this."

Naydrad made an untranslatable Kelgian noise and continued eating. Prilicla maintained its stable hover above the table without comment, and Danalta was in the process of growing a pair of Melfan manipulators while the rest of its body resembled a lumpy green pyramid with a single eye on top.

"I'm still myself," he said to Murchison, "with just a shade of Gogleskan FOKT. I've been given the Protector case, among others, and that is what I wanted to talk to you about. Temporarily I'm an acting Diagnostician, with full responsibility and authority regarding treatment, and may call on any assistance I require. I do need help, badly, but I don't know exactly what kind as yet. Neither do I want to pester other Diagnosticians, even politely, and certainly not the Diagnostician-in-Charge of Pathology. So I shall have to be devious and approach Thornnastor through you, its chief assistant, to get the sort of advice I need."

Murchison watched his refueling operation for a moment without speaking, then she said seriously, "You don't have to be circumspect with Thornnastor, you know. It badly wants to be involved in the Protector case, and would have been placed in charge if it hadn't been for the fact that you were the Senior with firsthand experience of the beastie, and you were already being considered for Diagnostician status. Thorny will be happy to assist you in every way possible.

"In fact, if you don't ask for its help," she ended, smiling, "our Chief of Pathology will walk all over you with its six outsize feet."

"I, too, would like to assist you, friend Conway," Prilicla joined in. "But considering the massive musculature of the patient, my cooperation will not be close."

"And I," Danalta said.

"And I," Naydrad said, looking up from the green mess which its Kelgian taste buds were finding so delectable, "will continue doing as I'm told."

Conway laughed. "Thank you, friends." To Murchison, he said, "I'll go back to Pathology with you and talk to Thornnastor. And I'm not proud. If I were to mention the Gogleskan problem, and the FROB geriatrics, and the other odds and ends which—"

"Thornnastor," Murchison said firmly, "likes to know, and stick its outsize olfactory sensor into everything."

He felt much better after the meeting with the Chief of Pathology which, because the Tralthan's waking and sleeping cycle was much longer than that of an Earth-human, took the remainder of his duty period. Thornnastor was the biggest gossip in the hospital; it just could not keep any of its mouths shut, but its information on virtually every aspect of extraterrestrial pathology, as well as in many areas not considered to be within its specialty, was completely dependable.

Thornnastor wanted to know everything, and it was certainly not reticent, about anything.

"As you are already aware, Conway," it said ponderously as he was about to leave, "we Diagnosticians are generally held in high regard among the members of our profession, and the respect shown us, insofar as it can be shown in a madhouse like this, is tempered by pity for the psychological discomfort we experience, and an almost lighthearted acceptance of the medical miracles we produce.

"We are Diagnosticians and, as such, medical miracles are expected of us," the Tralthan went on. "But the production of true medical miracles, or radical surgical procedures, or the successful culmination of a line of xenobiological research, can be personally unsatisfying to certain types of doctor. I refer to those practitioners who, although able and intelligent and highly dedicated to their art, require a fair apportionment of credit for the work they do."

Conway swallowed. He had never before heard the Diagnostician-in-Chief of Pathology talk to him like this, and the words would have been more suited to a lecture on his personal shortcomings from the Chief Psychologist. Was Thornnastor, knowing of his fondness for reaching solutions and initiating treatments with the minimum of consultation, suggesting that he was a grandstander and was therefore unsuitable material for a Diagnostician? But apparently not.

"As a Diagnostician one rarely obtains complete satisfaction from producing good work," the Tralthan went on, "because one can never be wholly sure that the work performed or the ideas originated are one's own. Admittedly the Educator tapes furnish other-species memory records only, but purely imaginary personality involvement with the tape donor leaves one feeling that any credit due for new work should be shared. If the doctor concerned is in possession of three, five, perhaps ten, Educator tapes, well, the credit is spread very thinly."

"But nobody in the hospital," Conway protested, "would dream of withholding the credit due a Diagnostician who had—"

"Of course not," Thornnastor broke in. "But it is the Diagnostician itself who withholds the credit, not its colleagues. Unnecessarily, of course, but that is one of the personal problems of being a Diagnostician. There are others, for the circumvention of which you will have to devise your own methods."

All four of the Tralthan's eyes had turned to regard Conway, a rare occurrence and proof that Thornnastor's vast mind was concentrating exclusively on his particular case. Conway laughed nervously.

"Then it is high time I visited O'Mara to take a few of those tapes," he said, "so that I will have a better idea of what my problems will be. I think initially a Hudlar tape, then a Melf and a Kelgian. When I'm accustomed, if I ever become accustomed to them, I'll request some of the more exotic..."

"Some of the mental stratagems used by my colleagues," Thornnastor continued ponderously, ignoring the interruption, "are such that they might conceivably tell their life-mates about them, but certainly no person with a lesser relationship. In spite of my overwhelming curiosity regarding these matters, they have not confided in me, and the Chief Psychologist will not open its files."

Two of its eyes curved away to regard Murchison and

it went on. "A few hours' or even days' delay in taking the tapes is not important. Pathologist Murchison is free to go, and I suggest that you take full advantage of each other while you are still able to do so without otherspecies psychological complications."

As they were leaving, Thornnastor added, "It is the Earth-human taped component of my mind which has suggested this..."

Chapter 11

"THE theory is that if you are to accustom yourself to the confusion of alien thought patterns," O'Mara growled at him as Conway was still rubbing the sleep out of his eyes, "it is better in the long run to confuse you a lot rather than a little at a time. You have been given the tapes during four hours of light sedation, during which you snored like a demented Hudlar, and you are now a five-way rugged individualist.

"If you have problems," the Chief Psychologist went on, "I don't want to know about them until you're absolutely sure they're insoluble. Be careful how you go and don't trip over your own feet. In spite of what your alter egos tell you to the contrary, you only have two of them."

The corridor outside O'Mara's office was one of the busiest in the hospital, with medical and maintenance staff belonging to a large variety of physiological classifications walking, crawling, wriggling, or driving past in both directions. Seeing his Diagnostician's armband and realizing, rightly in his case, that a certain amount of mental confusion and physical uncoordination might be present, they gave him as wide a berth as possible. Even the TLTU inside a pressure sphere mounted on heavy caterpillar treads passed him with more than a meter to spare.

A few seconds later a Tralthan Senior he knew passed by, but the big FGLI was not known to Conway's other selves, so his reaction time was slowed. When he swiveled his head to return the Tralthan's greeting, he was overcome suddenly by vertigo, because the Hudlar and Melf components of his mind were of beings whose heads did not swivel. Instinctively he reached toward the corridor wall to steady himself. But instead of a hard, tapering Hudlar tentacle or a shiny black Melfan pincer, the member supporting him was a flaccid pink object with five lumpy digits. By the time he had steadied himself both physically and mentally, he had become aware of an Earth-human DBDG in Monitor green waiting patiently to be noticed.

"You were looking for me, Lieutenant?" Conway asked.

"For the past couple of hours, Doctor," the officer replied. "But you were with the Chief Psychologist on a taping session and could not be disturbed."

Conway nodded. "What's the trouble?"

"Problems with the Protector," the Lieutenant said, and went on quickly. "The Exercise Room—that's what we're calling it now even though it still looks like a torture chamber—is underpowered. Tapping into the main power line for the section would necessitate going through four levels, only one of which is inhabited by warm-blooded oxygen-breathers. The structural alterations in the other three areas would be very time-consuming because of our having to guard against atmosphere contamination, especially where the Illensan chlorine-breathers are concerned. The answer would be a small power source sited within the Exercise Room. But if the Protector broke free, the shielding around the power unit might not survive, and if the shielding went, the radiation hazard would necessitate five levels'—above and below the area—being evacuated, and a lot more time would be wasted cleaning the —"

"The room is close to the outer hull," Conway said, feeling that a lot of time was being wasted right now by asking a medical man's advice on purely technical questions, and fairly simple ones at that. "Surely you can set up a small reactor on the outer hull, safe from the Protector, and run a line into—"

"That was the answer I came up with, too," the Lieutenant broke in, "but it gave rise to other problems, administrative rather than technical. There are regulations regarding what structures can and cannot be placed on the outer hull, and a reactor there, where one had never been before, might necessitate alterations in the hospital's external traffic flow patterns. In short, there is a major tangle of red tape which I can unravel given time, and if I asked all of the people concerned nicely and in triplicate. But you, Doctor, considering the urgency of your project, could *tell* them what you need."

Conway was silent for a moment. He was remembering one of the Chief Psychologist's remarks prior to the taping session and just before the sedation had taken effect. O'Mara had smiled sourly and said, "You have the rank now, Conway, even though it may turn out to be temporary. Go out and use it, or even abuse it. Just let me see you doing something with it."

Striving to make his tone that of a Diagnostician to whom nobody in the hospital would say no, Conway said, "I understand, Lieutenant. I'm on my way to Hudlar Geriatric, but I'll deal with it at the first communicator I pass. You have another problem?"

"Of course I have problems," the Lieutenant replied. "Every time you bring a new patient to the hospital, the whole maintenance division grows ulcers! Levitating brontosaurs, Drambon rollers, and now a patient who hasn't even been born yet inside a . . . a berserker!"

Conway looked at the other in surprise. Usually the Monitor Corps officers were faultless in matters of discipline and respect toward their superiors, whether military or medical. Drily, he said, "We can treat ulcers."

"My apologies, Doctor," the other said stiffly. "I've been in charge of a squad of Kelgians for the past two years, and I've forgotten how to be polite."

"I see." Conway laughed. Since he was carrying a Kelgian tape himself right then, the Lieutenant had his sympathy. "That problem I cannot help you with. Are there others?"

"Oh, yes," the other replied. "They are insoluble, but minor. The two Hudlars are still objecting to their continuous beating of the Protector. I asked O'Mara if he could find someone else for the job, someone who would suffer less mental distress while carrying it out. O'Mara told me that if such a person had escaped his screening and was currently working in the hospital, he would resign forthwith. So I'm stuck with the Hudlars, and their damn music, until the new accommodation is ready.

"They insist that it helps keep their minds off what they're doing, but have you ever had to listen to Hudlar music, continuously, day after day?"

Conway admitted that he had not had that experience, that a few minutes of it had been more than enough for him.

They had arrived at the interlevel lock, and he began climbing into one of the lightweight suits for the journey through the foggy yellow levels of the Illensan chlorine-breathers and the water-filled wards of the aquatic denizens of Chalderescol which lay between him and the Hudlar wards. He double-checked all the fastenings and reread the checklist, even though he had donned such pieces of hospital equipment thousands of times and could do it with his eyes shut. But he was not entirely himself just then, and the regulations stated that all medical personnel carrying Educator tapes, and as a consequence laboring under a degree of mental confusion, must use the checklist with their eyes wide open.

The Lieutenant was still standing patiently beside him. Conway said, "There's more?"

The officer nodded. "A fairly easy one, Doctor. Hardin, the Dietician-in-Chief, is asking about the consistency of the Protector's food. He says he can reproduce a synthetic mush tailored to fit its dietary requirements in all respects, but that there is a psychological aspect to the ingestion of food which may be important to the overall well-being of this particular patient. You had a brief telepathic contact with one of them and so have firsthand information on the subject. He would like advice."

"I'll talk to him later," Conway said, pausing before pulling the helmet over his head. "But in the meantime you can tell him that it rarely eats vegetation, and the food that it does eat is usually wrapped in a thick hide or exoskeleton and is fighting back. I suggest that he encases the food in long, hollow tubes with edible walls. The tubes can be incorporated into the exercise machinery and used to beat the patient in the interests of greater environmental realism. Its mandibles are capable of denting steel plating, and Hardin is right. It would not be happy eating the equivalent of thin, milky cereal."

He laughed again and added, "We wouldn't want to risk rotting its teeth."

The Hudlar Geriatric Ward was a comparatively new addition to Sector General's facilities, and it was the closest the hospital came to providing treatment for psychologically disturbed patients, and even then the treatment was available to only a statistically chosen few. This was because the solution to the problem, if one could be found, would have to be put into effect on a planet-wide scale on Hudlar itself.

The ward's artificial gravity had been set at the Hudlar normal of nearly four Earth-Gs, and the atmospheric pressure was a compromise which caused the minimum of inconvenience to both patients and nursing staff. There were three Kelgian nurses on duty, their fur twitching restlessly under their lightweight suits and gravity neutralizer harnesses as they sprayed nutrient paint onto three of the five patients. Conway buckled on a G-neutralizer suited to his Earth-human mass, signaled that he did not require a nurse to attend him, and moved toward the nearest unoccupied patient.

Immediately the Hudlarian component of his mind came surging up, almost obliterating the Melfan, Tralthan, Kelgian, and Gogleskan material and threatening to engulf Conway's own mind in a great wave of pity and helpless anger at the patient's condition.

"How are you today?" Conway asked ritually.

"Fine, thank you, Doctor," the patient replied, as he knew it would. Like the majority of other life-forms possessing immense strength, the Hudlarian FROBs were a gentle, inoffensive, and self-effacing race, none of whom would dream of suggesting that his medical ability was somehow lacking by saying that it was *not* well.

It was immediately obvious that the aging Hudlar was not at all well. Its six great tentacles, which normally supported its heavy trunk in an upright position for the whole of its waking and sleeping life, and which served as both manipulatory and ambulatory appendages, hung limply over the sides of its supporting cradle. The hard patches of callus, the knuckles on which it walked while its digits were curled inward to protect them against contact with the ground, were discolored and cracking. The digits themselves, usually so strong, rock-steady, and precise in their movements, were twitching continually into spasm.

The Hudlars lived in a heavy-gravity, high-pressure environment whose superdense air teemed with so much airborne vegetable and microanimal life-forms that it resembled a thick soup, which the inhabitants absorbed directly through the tegument of the back and flanks. But the absorption mechanism of the patient had begun to fail, so large areas of the skin were caked with discolored nutrient paint which would have to be washed off before the next meal could be sprayed on. But the condition was worsening, the patient's ability to absorb nourishment was diminishing, and that, in turn, was accelerating the deterioration in the skin condition.

Chemical changes caused by the incomplete absorption process caused the residual nutrient to smell. But even worse was the odor from the waste elimination area, no longer under voluntary control, whose discharge formed like milky perspiration on the patient's underside before dripping into the cradle's suction pan. Conway could not really smell anything at all, because his suit had its own air supply. But the FROB personality sharing his mind had experienced this situation many times in its life, and psychosomatic smells were, if anything, worse than the real kind.

The patient's mind was still clear, however, and there would be no physical deterioration in the brain structure until a few minutes after its double heart stopped beating, and therein lay the real tragedy. Rare indeed was the Hudlar mind that could remain stable inside a great body which was disintegrating painfully all around it, especially when the mind was fully and intensely aware of the process.

Hopelessly he searched for an answer, going through the material on gereology available at the time his tapes were donated as well as the painful data associated with his own childhood memories and subsequent medical experience. But there was no answer to be found anywhere in his multiple mind, and the consensus of all of them was that he should increase the dosage of painkilling medication so as to make the patient as comfortable as possible.

While he made the addition to the treatment chart, the Hudlar's speaking membrane vibrated stiffly, but that organ, too, was deteriorating, and this time the sounds it made were too distorted for his translator to make any sense of them. He murmured reassurances, which they both knew to be empty, and moved to the next cradle.

Its condition was fractionally better than the previous one, and its conversation with him was animated and covered every subject under the Hudlar sun except what ailed it. Conway was not fooled, much less his Hudlarian alter ego, and he knew that this particular FROB was enjoying—although that was scarcely the right word in these circumstances—its last few hours of sanity. The next two patients did not speak to him at all, and the last one was loudly articulate but no longer sane.

Its speaking membrane was vibrating continually inside the wide, cylindrical muffler which had been attached to reduce both the sound and the mental discomfort of those within earshot, but enough was escaping to make Conway feel very uncomfortable indeed. It was in poor physical shape as well. In addition to the breakdown of the absorption system over a large area of the body surface, the incontinence, and the marked deterioration evident in all of the limb extremities, two of the tentacles had lost mobility and resembled nothing so much as a couple of withered tree-trunks.

"Those limbs require urgent surgical attention, Doctor," the nurse engaged in spraying the patient with nutrient said, having first turned off its translator. In the forthright manner of all Kelgians it added, "Amputation is indicated to prolong the patient's life, if that is considered desirable."

In ordinary circumstances the prolongation of the patient's life was desirable and, in fact, was the prime consideration, and his mind was being flooded with information and suggestions for treating the equivalent condition in Melfans, Kelgians, Tralthans, and Earth-humans. But to the physiological classification FROB the very concept of curative medicine had been unknown until the discovery of Hudlar by the Federation, and to that species any major surgical intervention was hazardous in the extreme. On a heavy gravity, high-pressure world like Hudlar, the internal pressure and metabolic rate of its dominant life-form had to be correspondingly high.

The control of bleeding, both during a procedure and postoperatively, was difficult. And the internal decompression which was an unavoidable side effect of an operation could cause deformation and serious damage to major organs adjacent to the operative field. As a result the Hudlar information in his mind together with Conway's own experience of FROB surgery suggested caution, while the other mass of extraterrestrial experience advocated operating without delay. But a double amputation on a geriatric and dangerously weakened patient... Angrily he shook his head and turned away.

The Kelgian nurse was watching him closely. It said, "Does that movement of the cranium indicate a yes or a no answer to my question, Doctor?"

"It means that I haven't yet made up my mind," Conway said as he turned and escaped thankfully into the infants' ward.

While it was true that for the greater proportion of their lifetimes the Hudlars were impervious to disease and all but the most severe injuries—which was the primary reason why medicine had been an unknown science on their world—this did not hold during the first and final few years of life. His recent harrowing experience had shown all too clearly the ills to which aged Hudlars were prone, and now he was seeing the other and much less distressing end of the clinical spectrum.

Infant FROBs seemed to catch every Hudlarian pathogen present in their atmospheric soup until, if they were able to survive the first few encounters with them, their bodies built up the natural resistance which lasted for the greater part of their very long lives. Fortunately, the majority of the diseases were spectacular in their symptomology but individually nonfatal. Federation medical science had been able to provide cures for several of them and was working on the others. Unfortunately, while no single disease could be considered fatal in itself, all were potentially lethal because the ailments which the infants contracted were cumulatively weakening, and it was the order in which they were contracted and the number of diseases present at a given time which determined the lethality. A complete solution was not possible until specifics against all of the diseases were produced.

As Conway entered and looked around the furiously busy ward, the Hudlar material in his mind suggested that mass immunization was not the proper solution. There was a strong feeling that protecting the FROB children in that way would ultimately lead to a weakening of the species as a whole. But the Hudlar who had donated his tape had not been a member of the medical profession, there being no such profession on Hudlar, and had instead been a strange combination of philosopher, psychiatrist, and teacher. Even so, the feeling bothered Conway until a six-legged, half-ton infant came charging down on him shouting that it wanted to play, and drove everything from his mind but the need to take urgent evasive action.

He set his gravity controls to one-quarter G and jumped straight upward to the rail of the observation catwalk, barely two seconds before the young Hudlar hit the wall with a crash which must have severely tested both the ward's soundproofing and its structure. From his elevated viewpoint Conway could see that there were fewer than twenty patients in the ward, and in spite of the four Gs at floor level, they were all moving so fast that there seemed to be at least three times that number. When they occasionally stopped to change direction, he could see that the majority of them were displaying a variety of horrifying skin conditions.

An adult Hudlar with nutrient tanks strapped to its back finished spraying an infant it had cornered and immobilized at the far end of the ward, then turned and moved ponderously toward him.

It bore the insignia of a nurse-in-training, and it was, on this duty at least, little more than a baby-minder. But Conway knew that it was one of three FROBs undergoing medical training at Sector General, and the first members of that species chosen to introduce to their world the concepts of preventive and curative medicine. It was in female mode a remarkably handsome specimen and, unlike the Kelgian nurse in the geriatrics section, very polite and respectful.

"May I help you, Doctor?" it said, looking up at him. A sudden rush of memories from his alter ego's life on Hudlar invaded his mind so that he could not speak.

"Patient Seven, young Metiglesh, the one who wanted to play with you," it went on, "is responding well to the new treatment devised by Diagnostician Thornnastor. I can quite easily immobilize it for you if you wish to make a scanner examination."

It would be easy, Conway thought wryly, for a Hudlar nurse. That was the reason why an FROB trainee was in charge there—it knew exactly how much force to use on the little terrors, while equally or higher-qualified nurses of other species would be afraid to use the amount of force required in case they might injure the patients.

Young Hudlars were incredibly tough, and some of the adults were unbelievably beautiful.

"I'm just passing through, Nurse," he managed to say finally. "You seem to have everything under control here."

As Conway stared down at the being, his own knowledge of the FROB classification was being augmented by data on what it actually felt like to be a Hudlar in the male mode, as the donor had been at the time of making its tape, and he had memories only slightly less intense of being a female. He could remember the arrival of a recent offspring and how the birth process had drastically altered the hormone balance so that he became a male again. On Hudlar they were uniquely fortunate in that both life-mates were enabled to have their children in turn.

"Many life-forms carrying the Hudlar physiology tape visit here from the geriatric section," the nurse went on, unaware of the mental havoc it was causing him. His Hudlar alter ego was bringing up data, memories, experiences, wish-fulfillment fantasies of courtship, love-play, and of gargantuan couplings which made his Earth-human mind recoil in horror. But it was not Conway's mind that had control just then.

He tried desperately to regain possession, to fight against the overwhelming waves of raw instinct which were making it impossible for him to think. He tried to look only at his thinly gloved, non-Hudlar digits as they gripped the guardrail while the nurse went on. "It is distressing for a Hudlar, or for an entity bearing the Hudlar tape, to visit the geriatric section. I myself would not enter unless requested to do so, and I have the greatest respect and admiration for those of you who do so purely out of a sense of professional duty. Coming in here, it is said, frequently helps the overly distressed mind to think of something more pleasant.

"You are, of course, at liberty to remain as long as you deem necessary, Doctor. For whatever reason," it added sympathetically. "And if there is anything I can do to help you, you have only to ask."

His Hudlar component was doing its equivalent of baying at the moon. Conway croaked something which his translator was probably unable to handle and began moving along the catwalk toward the exit at a near run.

For Heaven's sake get control of yourself, he raged silently at himself. *It's six times bigger than you are!...*

Chapter 12

THE Menelden system was no stranger to catastrophe. It had been discovered some sixty years earlier by a Monitor Corps scoutship whose Captain had exercised the traditional right to name it because there were no indications that the system harbored indigenous intelligent life with its own name for the world. If such life had been present in the distant past, then all traces of it had been obliterated when a large, planet-size chunk of metal ore entered the system, colliding with the largest outer planet and causing havoc and ultimately further collision with the others, all in tight orbits around their primary.

When the system eventually restabilized itself, Menelde was an aging yellow sun tightly surrounded by a rapidly spinning cloud of asteroids, a large proportion of which were solid metal. Immediately following its discovery, life came to the Menelden system in the shape of mining and metal processing complexes and their operating crews from all over the Federation, and in that cosmic illustration of the Brownian movement of gases, accidents occurred.

The details of one did not become known until many weeks later, nor was the final responsibility for it ever determined.

An enormous multispecies accommodation module for

housing mining and metal-processing workers was being moved by tugs from an exhausted area to a fresh one, and was ponderously following a path between the slowly moving or relatively motionless asteroids and the other mining traffic which was engaged in similar delicate exercises in three-dimensional navigation.

One of the vessels, whose course would take it safely but uncomfortably close to the accommodation module and its tugs, was a carrier fully loaded with finished metal girders and sheets. Between the thrusters aft and the tiny control module forward the structure of the carrier was completely open to facilitate the loading and unloading of its cargo. This meant that the clearly visible mass of metal held, apparently none too securely, to its lashing points was exerting undue psychological pressure on the senior tug captain, who told the carrier captain to sheer off.

The carrier captain demurred, insisting that they would pass in perfect safety, while his ship and the vast accommodation module crept ponderously toward each other. The senior tug captain, who was charged with the safety of a structure incapable of independent maneuver and containing more than one thousand people, as opposed to the carrier with its three-man crew, had the last word.

Very slowly, because of the tremendous weight and inertia of its cargo, the carrier began to swing broadside-on to the module, intending to use its main thrusters to drive it clear long before their paths could intersect. The two vessels were closing, but slowly. There was plenty of time.

It was at that point that the accommodation module's supervisor, although not really worried, decided that it would be a very good time to hold an emergency drill.

The urgent flashing of hazard lights and the braying of alarm sirens, heard in the background while he was in communication with the module, must have had an unsettling effect on the senior tug captain. He decided that the carrier was turning too slowly and despatched two of his tugs to assist the process with their pressor beams. In spite of the caustic reassurances from the carrier captain that there was ample time for the maneuver and that everything was under control, the carrier was quickly pushed broadside-on to the approaching module—the position from which a brief burn on its thrusters would take it clear within a few seconds.

The thrusters did not fire.

Whether the failure was due to the effect of the hastily focused pressor beams on the carrier's uncovered control linkages which ran between the crew pod and the thrusters astern—they may well have been warped into immobility—or Fate had decreed that the system would malfunction at precisely that moment would never be known. But there were still a few minutes remaining before the collision would occur.

Ignoring the orderly confusion on board the module, where the supervisor was trying desperately to make his people realize that the practice emergency drill had suddenly become a real one, the carrier used its attitude control jets at maximum overload in an attempt to return the vessel to its original and safe heading. But the tremendous weight of a ship fully laden with a cargo of dense metal was too much for them, and slowly, almost gently, the stern of the carrier made contact with the forward section of the accommodation module.

The carrier, whose structure had been designed to withstand loadings only in the vertical plane, broke up when subjected to the sudden, lateral shock. Gigantic lengths of metal tore free from their lashing points, the metal retaining bands snapping like so much thread, and the long, open racks which held the sheet metal disintegrated with the collapse of the ship's main structure, sending their contents spinning toward the accommodation module's side like a slow-moving flight of throwing-knives. And mixed with the spinning metal plates and beams and pieces of the carrier's structure was the radioactive material of its power pile.

Many of the plates struck the module edge-on, inflicting long, deep incisions several hundred meters long in the hull before bouncing away again. The metal beams smashed against the already weakened hull, opening dozens of compartments to space, or drove deep into the module's interior like enormous javelins. The collision abruptly checked the structure's forward motion and left it a slowly spinning half-wreck, which presented in turn a flank which was unmarked and another which showed a scene of utter devastation.

One of the tugs took off after the expanding cloud of metal which had been the carrier and its cargo, to chart its course for later retrieval and to search for possible survivors among its crew. The remaining tugs checked the spin on the accommodation module, then gave what help they could until the emergency teams from nearby mining installations, and ultimately *Rhabwar*, arrived.

Except for a few Hudlars who were not inconvenienced by vacuum conditions, and a number of Tralthans who could also survive airlessness for short periods by going into hibernation mode and sealing all their body orifices, nobody along the stricken side of the module had survived. Even the immensely strong and tough-skinned Hudlars and Tralthans could not live in zero pressure when their bodies had been traumatically opened to space, and massive explosive decompression was not a condition which could be cured, even in Sector General.

The Hudlar and Tralthan quarters had suffered worst in the collision. Elsewhere the structure had retained its air even though the emergency drill condition meant that the occupants were in spacesuits anyway, so a pressure drop would not have been a problem. But in these areas it was the sudden deceleration and spin following the collision which had caused the casualties—hundreds of them which, because of the protection given by the suits, were serious rather than critical. When the module's artificial gravity was restored, the majority of these were treated by the Menelden complex's same-species medics and held in makeshift wards to await transfer to their home planets for further treatment or recuperation.

Only the really serious cases were sent to Sector General.

News of the Menelden accident had reached the hospital just in time to allow Conway to avoid having to face another serious problem, although regarding a major accident as a handy excuse for postponing a particularly worrying meeting was, he thought, neither admirable nor unselfish.

His Educator tapes were becoming so well established that it was difficult to tell when a set of feelings and reactions were his own or those of one or all of the Others. So much so that the next meeting with Murchison, when they would be together in their quarters in circumstances which would inevitably lead to physical intimacy, was something he had been dreading with increasing intensity as their next off-duty period drew closer. He just did not know how he would react to her, how much if any control he would have of the situation, and, most important of all, how she would react to his reactions.

Then suddenly *Rhabwar* was despatched to the Menelden system to coordinate the rescue operation and bring back the more serious casualties, and Murchison, a key member of its medical team, was on board.

Conway was greatly relieved, at first. But as the ship's former medical team leader he was aware of the danger she was in, from the kind of accident which could so easily occur during a large-scale rescue mission, and he began to worry. Instead of being glad that he would not have to see her for a day or so, he found himself heading for the casualty reception lock just before the ambulance ship was due to dock after its first return trip.

He spotted Naydrad and Danalta standing by the transfer lock and keeping well clear of the casualty reception team, who needed no help at all in doing their job.

"Where is Pathologist Murchison?" Conway asked as a litter containing what looked like a Tralthan multiple traumatic amputation went past. The FGLI tape material in his mind was pushing to the fore, urgently suggesting methods of treatment for this patient. Conway shook his head in an instinctive attempt to clear it, and said more firmly, "I want to see Murchison."

Beside the uncharacteristically silent Naydrad, Danalta began to assume the bodily contours of an Earth-human female similar in shape and size to that of the pathologist.

Then, sensing Conway's disapproval, it slumped back into shapelessness.

"Is she on board?" Conway asked sharply.

The nurse's fur was rippling and pulling itself into irregular patterns of tufting in a manner which, to his Kelgian alter ego, indicated an extreme reluctance to answer combined with the expectation of unpleasantness.

"I have a Kelgian tape," he said quietly, pointing at the other's telltale fur. "What's bothering you, Nurse?"

"Pathologist Murchison chose to remain at the disaster site," Naydrad replied finally, "to assist Doctor Prilicla with the triage."

"The *triage*!" Conway burst out. "Prilicla shouldn't be subjecting itself to . . . Dammit, I'd better go out there and help. There are more than enough doctors here to treat the casualties and if . . . You have an objection?"

Naydrad's fur was tufting and undulating in a new and more urgent sequence.

"Doctor Prilicla is the leader of the medical team," the Kelgian said. "Its proper place is at the disaster site, coordinating the rescue operation and disposition of casualties, regardless of the physical or mental trauma which might result. The presence of a former team leader could be considered as an implied criticism of its professional handling of the situation, which up until now has been exemplary."

Watching the movements of that expressive Kelgian fur, Conway was not really surprised at the strength of feeling that was being shown toward a superior who had been in the job for only a few days. By the nature of things, superiors were respected, sometimes feared, and usually obeyed with reluctance by their subordinates. But Prilicla had proved that it was possible to lead and instill absolute loyalty by making subordinates obey through another kind of fear, that of hurting the boss's feelings.

When Conway did not reply, Naydrad went on. "Your offer of assistance was foreseen, which is the reason why Pathologist Murchison remained to help Prilicla. The Cinrusskin's empathic faculty does not, as you well know, require that it work in close proximity to the injured, so it can remain in comparative safety while Murchison moves among the casualties as you would have done if you'd gone out there."

"Doctor," Danalta said, breaking its long silence, "Pathologist Murchison is in turn being assisted by several large, heavily muscled entities of its own and other species who are trained in heavy rescue techniques. These entities are charged with the responsibility for removing casualties from the wreckage at the Pathologist's direction, and for seeing that the same wreckage does not endanger Murchison.

"I mention this, Doctor," Danalta added, "so as to reassure you regarding the safety of your life-mate."

The polite and respectful tone of Danalta sounded almost obsequious after that of the more blunt-spoken Naydrad. But the TOBS, too, had developed a measure of empathy as a necessary adjunct to their species' faculty for defensive and offensive protective mimicry, and respectfulness made a nice change whether it was real or simulated.

"Thank you, Danalta. That is considerate of you," Conway said, but then turned to Naydrad. "But Prilicla, on triage!..."

The thought of it was enough to make Conway, and anyone else who knew the little empath, cringe.

The range and sensitivity of the Cinrusskin's empathic faculty had been invaluable when the empath had been a member of *Rhabwar*'s medical team, and now that Prilicla was heading that team the same circumstances would apply. The empath could feel among the casualties of a wrecked ship, especially those who were physically motionless, grievously injured and apparently lifeless, and state with absolute accuracy which protective suits held cadavers and which still-living survivors. It did so by attuning itself to the residual emotional radiation of the casualty's often deeply unconscious brain, and by feeling what the survivor's unconscious mind felt and analyzing the results, it could decide whether there was any hope of reviving the spark of life which remained. Space accidents had to be dealt with quickly if there was to be anyone left alive to rescue, and on countless occasions Prilicla's empathic faculty had saved vital time and a great many lives.

A high price had to be paid for this ability, because Prilicla had in many cases to suffer with each of the casualties, for a short or a lengthy period, before such diagnoses or assessments could be made. But triaging the Menelden accident would mean encountering emotional distress of a whole new order of magnitude, so far as Prilicla was concerned. Fortunately, Murchison's feelings toward the little empath could only be described as fanatically maternal, and she would ensure that the storm of emotional radiation—the pain and panic and grief of the injured and their bereaved friends—which raged within that devastated accommodation module was experienced by the empath at the longest possible range, and for the shortest possible duration.

Triage called for the presence of a Senior Surgeon at the disaster site. Prilicla was one of the hospital's finest surgeons, and it was being assisted by a pathologist who was second only to those of Diagnostician rank. Together they should be able to do that particularly harrowing job of casualty assessment without delay or indecision.

They would be following procedures laid down in the distant past to cover large-scale medical emergencies, from the time when air attacks, bombardments, terrorist bombings, and similar effects of the interracial mass psychosis called war had added unnecessarily to the death tolls of purely natural disasters. At times like these, medical resources could not be wasted, or time and effort devoted to hopeless cases. That had been the thinking behind triage.

Casualties were assessed and placed into three groups. The first contained the superficially or nonfatally injured, those suffering from psychological trauma, the people who would not die should treatment be delayed and who could wait until transportation was available to their home-planet hospitals. The second group comprised those beings who were so seriously injured that their condition would prove fatal no matter what was done for them, and who could only be made as comfortable as possible until they terminated. The third and most important of the groups contained those whose injuries were grievous, but who stood a fair chance of survival if the indicated treatment could be given without delay.

It was the Group Three injuries which were being sent to Sector General, Conway thought as he watched another litter go by with its pressure envelope inflated and its organic contents so hidden by life-support equipment that it was difficult even to be sure of its physiological classification. His own opinion was that this was a borderline case between Groups Two and Three.

"That is the last casualty on this trip, Doctor," said Naydrad quickly. "We must leave at once to bring back another batch."

The Kelgian turned and began undulating towards *Rhabwar*'s boarding tube. Danalta's shape became that of a dark green ball again, featureless except for an eye and a mouth which regarded him and spoke.

"You will already have noticed, Doctor," it said, "that Senior Physician Prilicla has a very high regard for the surgical ability of its colleagues and it is, moreover, extremely averse to placing any of the casualties in the hopeless category."

The mouth smoothed out and the eye withdrew as the TOBS rolled quickly away in Naydrad's wake.

Chapter 13

HE learned of the return of *Rhabwar* with its last batch of Menelden casualties as he was about to attend his first Meeting of Diagnosticians. As he was the most recent probationary member, his sudden withdrawal for the purpose of exchanging a few words with Murchison would most certainly be considered impolite and downright insubordinate, and so their next meeting would again be delayed. His feelings about that were mostly of relief, and of shame at feeling relieved. He took his place, not expecting to make any important contribution to such august proceedings.

Nervously he looked across at O'Mara, the only other non-Diagnostician present, who sat dwarfed by the massive Thornnastor on one side and the coldly radiating spherical pressure envelope of Semlic, the SNLU methane-breathing Diagnostician from the cold levels. The Chief Psychologist stared back at him without expression. The features of the other Diagnosticians ranged around the room, sitting, crouching, hanging from or otherwise occupying the furniture designed for their bodily comfort, were likewise unreadable even though several of them were watching him.

Ergandhir, one of the Melfan ELNTs present, spoke first. "Before we discuss the Menelden casualties to be assigned to us, work which of necessity has the greatest priority, are there any less urgent matters requiring general discussion and guidance? Conway, as the most recent recruit to the ranks of the voluntary insane, you must be encountering a few problems."

"A few," Conway agreed. Hesitantly, he added, "At

present they are mechanical, temporarily beyond my scope, or completely insoluble."

"Please specify," an unidentified entity said at the other side of the room. It could have been one of the Kelgians, whose speaking orifices barely moved during a conversation. "It is to be hoped that all of these problems are temporarily insoluble."

For a moment Conway felt like a junior intern again, being criticized by a senior tutor for loose and emotional thinking, and the criticism was well deserved. He had to get a grip on himself and start thinking straight, with all five of his minds.

He said clearly, "The mechanical problems arise from the necessity of providing a suitable environment and treatment facilities for the Protector of the Unborn, before it gives birth and—"

"Pardon the interruption, Conway," Semlic broke in, "but it is unlikely that we can help directly with this problem. You were instrumental in rescuing the being from its wrecked ship, you had brief telepathic communication with the intelligent embryo, and you are therefore the only entity with sufficient firsthand knowledge to solve it. May I say, with sympathy, that you are welcome to this problem."

"While I cannot help you directly," Ergandhir joined in, "I can make available physiological and behavioral data on a similar Melfan life-form which, like the young Protector, is born fully formed and capable of defending itself. Birth takes place only once in the parent's lifetime, and there are invariably four young as a result. They attack and endeavor to eat the parent, who usually manages to defend itself sufficiently well if not to survive, then at least to kill one or two of its offspring, who sometimes try to kill one another. Were this not so they would long since have overrun my planet. The species is not sentient..."

"Thank heaven for that," O'Mara murmured.

"...Or ever likely to become so," Ergandhir went on. "I have studied your reports on the Protector with great interest, Conway, and shall be pleased to discuss this material with you if you think it might be helpful. But you mentioned other problems."

Conway nodded as the Melfan material in his mind surfaced with pictures of the tiny, lizardlike creatures which infested the food-growing areas of Melf, and which had survived in spite of the most large-scale and sophisticated efforts at extermination. He could see the parallels between them and the Protectors, and would certainly talk to the Melfan Diagnostician as soon as the opportunity arose.

He went on. "The apparently insoluble problem is Goglesk. This is not an urgent problem, except to me, because there is personal involvement. For this reason I should not waste your time by—"

"I was not aware," one of the two Illensan PVSJs present said, twitching restively inside its chlorine envelope, "that a Gogleskan tape was available."

Conway had forgotten for a moment that "personal involvement" was one of the phrases used by Diagnosticians and tape-bearing Senior Physicians to inform each other that their minds were carrying the memory-record of a member of the species under discussion. Before he could reply, O'Mara spoke quickly.

"There is no tape available," he said. "The memory transfer was accidental and involuntary, and occurred when Conway was visiting the planet. He may wish to discuss the details with you at some future date, but I agree with him that such a discussion now would be time-consuming and inconclusive."

They were all staring at him, but it was Semlic, who had changed lenses on its external vision pickup so as to see him more closely, who asked the question first.

"Am I to understand that you possess a memory record which cannot be erased, Conway?" it said. "This is a most disquieting thought for me. I myself am gravely troubled by my overcrowded mind and have seriously considered returning to Senior Physician status by drastically reducing the number of my tapes. But my alter egos are guests who can always be forced to leave should their presence become unbearable. But one memory record in permanent residence, without the possibility of erasure, is more than enough. None of your colleagues would think any less highly of you if you were to do as I am about to do and have the other tapes erased..."

"Semlic has been about to do that," O'Mara said quietly, with his translator switched off so that only Conway could hear him, "every few days for the past sixteen years. But it is right. If there are serious problems as a result of the Gogleskan presence reacting against the others, erase them. There would be no discredit attached, no inadequacy of personality implied, and it would, in fact, be the sensible course. But then, nobody could describe you as being sensible."

"...And among my mind-guests," Semlic was saying when Conway returned his attention to the SNLU, "are a number of entities who have had, well, very interesting and unorthodox lives. With all this nonmedical experience available I may be able to advise you should you encounter personal problems with Pathologist Murchison—"

"With *Murchison*!..." Conway said, incredulously.

"It is possible," Semlic replied, missing or ignoring the overtones. "All here have the greatest respect for its professional competence and its personal disposition, and I, personally, would not like to think that it would suffer any emotional trauma because I had omitted to advise you, Conway. You are fortunate indeed to have such an entity as your life-mate. Naturally, I have no personal physical interest in this being..."

"I'm relieved to hear that," Conway said, looking frantically to O'Mara for help. It was beginning to sound as if the SNLU Diagnostician was going out of its supercooled, crystalline mind. But the Chief Psychologist ignored him.

"...My enthusiasm stems from the DBDG Earth-human tape which has been occupying an undue portion of my mind since I began talking to you," the SNLU went on, "and which belonged to a very fine surgeon who was inordinately fond of activities associated with reproduction. For this reason I find your DBDG female most disturbing. It possesses the ability to communicate nonverbally, and perhaps unconsciously, during ambulation, and the mammary area is particularly—"

"With me," Conway broke in hastily, "it is that Hudlar trainee in the FROB infants' ward."

It turned out that several of the Diagnosticians present were carrying Hudlar physiology tapes and were not averse to discussing the nurse's professional competence and physical attributes at length, but the SNLU cut them short.

"This discussion must be giving Conway the wrong impression about us," Semlic said, its external vision pickups swiveling to include everyone in the room. "It might conceivably lower the high opinion Conway has of Diagnosticians, whose deliberations it would expect to be on a more rarefied professional level. Let me reassure it on your behalf that we are simply showing our latest potential member that the majority of its problems are not new and have been solved, in one way or another, and usually with the help of colleagues who are more than willing to assist it at any time."

"Thank you," Conway said.

"Judging by the continued silence of the Chief Psychologist," Semlic went on, "you must be coping fairly well up to now. But there is some small assistance I may be able to render you, and it is environmental rather than personal. You may visit my levels at any time, the only proviso being that you remain in the observation gallery.

"Few, indeed, are the warm-blooded, oxygen-breathers who take a professional interest in my patients," the SNLU added, "but if you should be the exception, then special arrangements will have to be made."

"No, thank you," Conway said. "I could not make any useful contribution to subzero crystalline medicine just now, if ever."

"Nevertheless," the methane-breather went on, "should you visit us, be sure to increase your audio sensitivity and switch off your translator, then listen. A number of your warm-blooded colleagues have derived a certain amount of comfort from the result."

"Cold comfort," O'Mara said drily, and added, "We

are devoting an unfair proportion of our time to Conway's personal problems rather than to those of his patients."

Conway looked around at the others, wondering how many of them were carrying FROB physiology tapes. He said, "There is the Hudlar geriatric problem. Specifically, the decision whether to involve the patient in a dangerous multiple amputation procedure which, if successful, will prolong life for a comparatively short time, or to allow nature to take its course. In the former event the quality of the prolonged life leaves much to be desired."

Ergandhir's beautifully marked exoskeletal body moved forward in its frame, and the lower mandible moved in time with its translated words. "That is a situation I have run against many times, as have we all, and with species other than the Hudlars. The result in my own case has been, to use a Melfan metaphor, a badly chipped carapace. Essentially it is an ethical decision, Conway."

"Of course it is!" one of the Kelgians said before Conway could reply. "The decision will be a close and personal one. However, from my knowledge of the doctor concerned the probability is that Conway will opt for surgical intervention rather than a clinical observation of the patient to the terminal phase."

"I am inclined to agree," Thornnastor said, speaking for the first time. "If a situation is inherently hopeless, it is better to do something rather than nothing. And with an operating environment making it difficult for other species to work effectively, an experienced Earth-human surgeon might expect good results."

"Earth-human DBDGs are not the best surgeons in the Galaxy," the Kelgian joined in again, its rippling fur indicating to those carrying DBLF tapes the feelings which were concealed by its unsubtle mode of speech. "The Tralthans, Melfans, Cinrusskins, we Kelgians are more surgically adept in certain circumstances. But there are situations where this dexterity cannot be brought to bear because of environmental conditions . . ."

"The operating theater must suit the patient," a voice broke in, "and not the doctor."

". . . Or physiological factors in the surgeon," the Kelgian went on. "Protective garments or vehicles required to work in hostile environments inhibit the finer movements of manipulatory appendages and digits, and remotely controlled manipulators lack precision or are subject to malfunction at the most critical times. The DBDG hand, however, can be protected against a large number of hostile environments by a ridiculously thin glove which does not inhibit digital movements, and the supporting musculature is such that they can operate with minimal loss of efficiency in the presence of elevated pressure and gravity. The hands remain operational even when projecting a short distance beyond the field of the gravity nullifiers. Although crudely formed and comparatively restricted in their movements, the DBDG hands can go anywhere, surgically speaking, and—"

"Not everywhere, Conway," Semlic broke in. "I'll thank you to keep your superheated hands off *my* patients."

"Diagnostician Kursedth is being diplomatic, for a Kelgian," Ergandhir said. "It is complimenting you while explaining why you are likely to get more than your share of the nasty jobs."

"I guessed as much," Conway said, laughing.

"Very well," Thornnastor said. "We shall now consider the urgent matter of the Menelden casualties. If you will kindly regard your displays, we will discuss their present clinical condition, projected treatment and the assignments of surgical responsibility..."

The polite inquiries, sympathy, and advice which, Conway now realized, had cloaked a searching examination of his feelings and professional attitudes, were over for the time being. Thornnastor, the hospital's most experienced and senior Diagnostician, had taken charge of the meeting.

"...You can see that the majority of the cases," the Tralthan went on, "have been assigned to Senior Physicians of various physiological classifications whose capabilities are more than equal to the tasks. Should unforeseen difficulties arise, one of ourselves will be called on to assist. A much smaller number of casualties, the really nasty cases, will be our direct responsibility. Some of you have been given only one of these patients, for reasons which will become obvious when you study the case notes, and others have been given more. Before you begin organizing your surgical teams and planning the procedures in detail, are there any comments?"

For the first few minutes they were all too busy studying the details of the cases assigned to them to have anything useful to say, and the initial comments were more in the nature of complaints.

"These two cases you've given me, Thornnastor," Ergandhir said, tapping one of its hard, sharply tapered pincers against its display screen. "They have so many compound and comminuted fractures between them that if they survive at all, they will be carrying so much wiring, pins, and plating that induction will elevate their body temperatures every time they approach a power generator. And what were two Orligian DBDGs doing there anyway?"

"Wreckage subsistence casualties," the pathologist replied. "They were members of the rescue team from the nearby Orligian processing plant. You are always complaining that you never get enough DBDG surgical experience."

"You've given me just one case," Diagnostician Vosan said. The Crepellian octopod turned to regard Thornnastor, then it made a noise which did not translate before adding, "Rarely have I seen such a discouraging clinical picture, and I shall certainly have my hands full, all eight of them, with this one."

"It was the number and dexterity of your manipulatory appendages," Thornnastor replied, "which impelled me to assign the case to you in the first place. But the time for discussion grows short. Are there any other comments before we move to procedures?"

Ergandhir said quickly, "During the intercranial work, on one of my patients in particular, emotional radiation monitoring would be distinctly advantageous."

"And I," Vosan said, "would find it useful during the preoperative phase to check on the level of unconsciousness and required anesthesia."

"And I! And I!" clamored several of the others, and for a moment there were too many voices talking at once for the translators to handle them. Thornnastor gestured for silence.

"It seems," the Tralthan said, "that the Chief Psychologist must remind you once again of the physiological and psychological capabilities of our one and only medically qualified empath. Major?"

O'Mara cleared his throat and said drily, "I have no doubt that Doctor Prilicla would be willing and anxious to help all of you, but as a Senior Physician who is being considered for elevation to Diagnostician status, it is in the best position to judge where and when its empathy can be used to best effect. There is also the fact that while it is useful to have an empathic sensitive constantly monitoring the condition of a deeply unconscious patient during an operation, the patient does not really require it and the only benefit lies in the mental comfort and reassurance of the surgeon.

"There is also the fact," the Chief Psychologist went on, ignoring the untranslatable sounds of protest from around the table, "that our empath functions best when among people who like and fully understand it. This being so, it should be clear to you that Prilicla is allowed a wide degree of latitude in its choice, not only in the cases it takes but in the surgeons it agrees to assist. And so, if the person who has worked with Senior Physician Prilicla since it joined us as a junior intern, and who helped it during its early medical training, if this doctor requested the assistance of Prilicla during an operation, it would not be refused. Isn't that so, Conway?"

"I, yes, I expect so," Conway stammered. He had not been listening closely for the past few minutes, because his mind had been on his cases, his close to hopeless cases, and on thoughts of open professional rebellion.

"Do you need Prilicla?" O'Mara asked quietly. "You have first refusal. If you do not need, as opposed to merely want, the assistance of your empathic friend, say so. A line of your colleagues who do need Prilicla will form rapidly on the left."

Conway thought for a moment, trying to coordinate and evaluate the input from his other mind components. Even the friendly and perpetually frightened Khone was radiating sympathy for his cases, and previously the mere sight of an uninjured Hudlar was sufficient to throw it into a panic reaction. Finally, he said, "I do not think that an empath would be of much help to these cases. Prilicla cannot work miracles, and at least three separate acts of supernatural intervention would be needed if these cases are to make it. And even then, well, I very much doubt that the patients or their close relatives will thank us."

"You can refuse the cases," O'Mara said quietly, "but you will have to give us a better reason than that they appear to be hopeless. As we have mentioned before, as a Diagnostician on probationary status you will be given what seems like an unfair share of such cases. This is to accustom you to the idea that the hospital must deal with partial successes and failures as well as nice, tidy, and complete cures. Up until now you have never had to concern yourself with problems of aftercare, have you, Conway?"

"I realize that," he replied angrily, because it sounded as though he was being criticized for past successes, or being accused of grandstanding in some obscure fashion. And then he began to wonder if his anger was due to there being a certain amount of truth in the accusation. More quietly, he went on, "Perhaps I've been lucky..."

"As well as surgically adept," Thornnastor interjected.

"...In the past with cases which could only be complete successes or utter failures," he went on. "But these patients... Even with the life-support systems in continuous operation it seems to me that they are only technically alive, and I would need Prilicla's empathic faculty simply to verify that fact."

"Prilicla sent these casualties to us," one of the Kelgians said who had not previously spoken. "Clearly, it did not consider them hopeless. Are you in difficulties deciding on procedure, Conway?"

"Certainly not!" Conway said sharply. He went on. "I know Prilicla and Cinrusskins tend to be incurable optimists. Unpleasant ideas like the thought of failure with a patient, or a case that is hopeless from the start, are utterly foreign to it. There have been times when it shamed me into feeling the same way. But now I am being realistic. It appears to me that two, perhaps three of these four cases are little more than not quite dead specimens for investigation by Pathology."

"At last you are showing signs of accepting your situation, Conway," Thornnastor said in its slow, ponderous voice. "You may never again be able to concentrate your entire mind and capabilities on a single patient, and you must learn to accept failure and make your failures contribute to your future successes. It is possible that you will lose all four of your patients, or you may save all of them. But no matter what procedure and treatment you decide upon, and the good or bad results which ensue, you will use your multiply augmented mind to learn whether or not that same mind is stable enough to endure and maintain control over your procedures, whether personally performed or delegated.

"You will also bear constantly in mind," the senior Diagnostician went on, "the fact that while treating your four cases from the Menelden emergency list, you have other concerns. The FROB geriatric problem, our presently unsatisfactory organ replacement postoperative difficulties, the approaching parturition of your Protector, and even, if its presence suggests a new viewpoint or procedure on any of these problems, the data provided by the nonerasable mind of your Gogleskan friend. And if you are bearing all these things in mind, and my own Earth-human mind partner is unhappy with that phrase because it is what your DBDGs call a pun, you have already realized that FROB replacement surgery will play a vital part in the treatment of your four cases, and any failure could provide ready access to the organs needed to ensure the success of a not quite so hopeless case.

"We all find it difficult to accept failure, Conway," Thornnastor continued, "and your past record will make it less easy for you. But these cases are not being assigned to you for psychological reasons. Your level of competence as a surgeon warrants—"

"What our overtalkative colleague is saying, once again," one of the Kelgians broke in, its fur tufting with impatience, "is that good doctors are given the worst patients. And now, may I discuss my two cases before they both terminate, from old age?"

Chapter 14

THE first three hours were spent on preparatory work, tidying up the traumatic amputations performed by flying metal at the accident site, charting the extent of the internal injuries, checking on the readiness of the operating teams, and, in spite of the cooling unit in his suit, sweating.

At this stage in the proceedings his work was chiefly supervisory, so his increased output of perspiration was unconnected with physical activity and was what O'Mara referred to as psychosomatic sweating, a condition which the Chief Psychologist would tolerate only on rare occasions.

When one of the patients died preoperatively, Conway's feelings lacked the intensity he had been expecting in that situation. The prognosis on that particular Hudlar had been very poor in any event, so when the sensors indicated termination it was not a surprise. The Melfan, Illensan, Kelgian, Tralthan, and Gogleskan components of his mind registered low-key professional regret at the loss; the Hudlar alter ego felt more strongly, but its sorrow was tinged with relief because it knew how drastically curtailed would have been the patient's quality of life had it survived, and because the other three cases were occupying so much of his attention, Conway's own reaction lay somewhere in between.

He maintained the cadaver's respiration and cardiac functions so that its undamaged organs and limbs, what few of them remained, would be in optimum condition for transplantation. A small part of his mind wondered if the Hudlar's parts were used for replacement surgery on its more fortunate colleagues, could it truly be considered to be dead? Which led, inevitably, to a minor conflict within his multiple mind between the Hudlar component and the others regarding the treatment of the physical remains after death.

For reasons which were not fully understood even by the members of the species themselves, the Hudlars, although in all other respects a race of highly intelligent, sensitive, and philosophically advanced beings, were unique in that they did not honor or show the slightest degree of respect for their recently deceased. The memory of the person while alive was treasured by its friends, and commemorated in various fashions, but these records invariably omitted any reference to the fact that the being concerned had died. The life and accomplishments of the entity were remembered; the death was studiously ignored, and the deceased disposed of quickly and without ceremony, as if it was a piece of unsightly litter.

In this case the Hudlar idiosyncrasy was a distinct advantage, because it removed the often time-consuming necessity for obtaining the consent of the next of kin for organ removal and transplant.

Realizing suddenly that he was mentally sidetracking himself and wasting time, Conway gave the signal to begin.

He joined the operating frame around FROB-Three, who was the patient with the fractionally better chance of making it, taking the observer's position beside Senior Physician Yarrence, the Kelgian surgeon who had charge of the team. His original intention had been to head the team on the recently deceased FROB-Eighteen's operation, but that patient's demise meant that he could now keep a close watch on the three operations, all of which were urgent and critical enough to require simultaneous rather than consecutive performance. The members of his original team had been divided up between Yarrence, Senior Physician Edanelt, the Melfan in charge of FROB-Ten, and the Tralthan Senior Hossantir who had taken FROB-Forty-three.

Even though the FROB life-form was capable of living and working in gravity-free and airless conditions, this was only possible when the immmensely tough and flexible tegument remained intact. When the skin had been pierced and the underlying blood vessels and organs exposed, as had occurred in several areas with this patient, deep surgery was impossible unless the natural gravity and pressure environment was reproduced. To do otherwise was to invite massive hemorrhaging and organ displacement due to the high pressure of the internal fluids. For this reason the OR staff were forced to wear gravity repulsors set to four Gs and heavy-duty protective suits whose gauntlets had been replaced by tight-fitting operating membranes designed to minimize the effects of the high external pressure.

They clustered around the patient like a shoal of ungainly fish, Conway thought, about to begin their surgical nibbling.

"The rear limbs have escaped with superficial damage and will heal naturally," Yarrence said, more for the benefit of his recorders than for Conway. "The two midlimbs and left forelimb have been lost, and the stumps will require surgical trimming and capping in preparation for the fitting of prosthetics. The right forelimb is still attached but has been so badly crushed that in spite of efforts to reestablish circulation to the affected areas, necrosis has taken place. This limb will also require removal and capping..."

The FROB in his mind stirred restively and seemed to be raising objections, but Conway did not speak because he had no clear idea of what it was objecting to.

"... Of the stump," the Kelgian Senior went on. "There is a metal splinter which has been driven into the right thoracic area with associated damage to a major vein, the bleeding from which has been incompletely controlled by the application of external pressure. This situation must be rectified urgently. There is also cranial damage, a large depressed fracture which is compressing the main nerve trunk and affecting mobility in the rear limbs. Subject to approval"... Yarrence glanced briefly in Conway's direction... "we shall remove the damaged forelimb, which will allow easier access for the team-members working in the cranial area, and prepare the stumps for—"

"No," Conway said firmly. He could not see anything but the Kelgian's conical head inside the heavy protective garment, but he could imagine the silvery fur tufting in anger as he went on. "Do not cap the forelimb stumps, but prepare them instead for a transfer and transplant of the rear limbs. Otherwise your procedure as outlined is approved."

"The risk to the patient is increased," Yarrence said sharply, "and the operational time will be extended by at least twenty percent. Is this desirable?"

Conway was silent for a moment, thinking about the quality of life of the patient following the success of the simple as opposed to the more complex operation. Compared with the immensely strong and precisely controlled forelimbs possessed by a normal FROB, the telescoping, hinged, and swiveling prosthetic was ridiculously weak and inefficient. As well, Hudlar amputees found them aesthetically displeasing and distressing when the forelimbs—which were the members most conveniently placed to the eyes and used for the more delicate physical manipulations, including the long and involved preliminaries to mating—were artificial. Transplanting the rear limbs forward, although risky considering the weakened state of the patient, was infinitely preferable, because if the operation were successful, it would provide the FROB with forelimbs which would be only fractionally less sensitive and precise than the originals. Since the limbs would be coming from the same entity, there would be no immune system involvement or tissue rejection problems.

The Hudlar material in Conway's mind was insisting

that he disregard the risks, while his own mind was trying desperately to find ways of reducing them.

He said, "Leave the forelimb transplant until the cranial and abdominal work is successfully completed; otherwise the transplant would be wasted effort. Don't forget to clean the tegument frequently and respray with anesthetic. In cases like this the absorption mechanism is affected by the general condition of—"

"I know that," Yarrence said.

"Of course you do," Conway went on. "You have the Hudlar tape, too, probably the same one as I have. The operation carries a strong element of risk, but it is well within your capabilities, and if the patient were conscious I have no doubt that—"

"It would want to take the risk, too," Yarrence broke in again. "But if the Hudlar in my mind feels that way, I, as the surgeon, feel obliged to express caution on its behalf. But I agree, Conway, the operation is desirable."

Conway detached himself from the operating frame, paying Yarrence the compliment of not watching the opening stages of the operation. In any case, incising an FROB's ultratough tegument required the tools of an engineering workshop rather than an operating theater, because the cauterization effects of using fine laser cutters, which were so necessary during internal surgery, seriously inhibited healing along the faces of tegument incisions. The blades which had to be used were two-handed Kelgian Six scalpels, and they required a lot of physical effort as well as a high degree of mental concentration in use, and frequently the medic was in greater danger from the blade than the patient. It was a good time to remove all unnecessary distractions from Yarrence, which included the presence of a would-be Diagnostician, and move to FROB-Ten.

It was obvious from the first look that this patient would never again see its home planet. Five of the six limbs had either been traumatically severed during the accident or damaged beyond the possibility of surgical reconstruction. In addition there was a deep incised wound in the left flank which had penetrated to and destroyed the function of the absorption organ on that side. Decompression, brief as it had been before the victim's self-sealing safety bubble had deployed inside its room, had damaged the organ's twin on the right side because of the sudden rush of body fluid toward the area which had been opened to zero pressure. As a result FROB-Ten was able to receive barely enough sustenance to continue living, providing that it did not exert itself in any way.

An FROB perpetually at rest was difficult to imagine. If such a thing were possible, it would certainly be a very unhappy Hudlar.

"A multiple replacement job," Senior Physician Edanelt said, curling an eye to regard Conway as he approached. "If we have to replace a major internal organ, there is no point in fitting prosthetic limbs rather than real ones. But it bothers me, Conway. My Hudlar alter ego suggests that we don't try too hard with this one, while my own purely selfish Melfan mind is concerned chiefly with gaining more other-species surgical experience."

"You are being too harsh with yourself," Conway said, then added thoughtfully, "At the same time, I'm very glad that the hospital discourages visits from patients' relatives. The postoperative talk with the patient, especially in a case like this one, is bad enough."

"If the prospect causes you serious mental distress," Edanelt said quickly, "I would willingly relieve you of it."

"Thank you, no," Conway said, feeling tempted. "It is supposed to be my job." He was, after all, the acting Diagnostician-in-Charge.

"Of course," said Edanelt. "Presumably the replacements are immediately available?"

"Patient Eighteen terminated a few minutes ago," Conway said. "The absorption and food-processing organs are intact, and there are three usable limbs. Thornnastor will let you have more as and when you need them. This was one accident which left us with no shortage of spare parts."

As he finished speaking, Conway attached himself to the operating frame beside Edanelt and began discussing the special problems which would be encountered with this case, and in particular the necessity for performing three major operations concurrently.

Because of the nature of FROB-Ten's injuries there was less than fifty percent of the patient's absorption system functioning, and that situation was being maintained with difficulty and with no certainty that there would not be further deterioration within the next few hours. The absorption mechanism could be used to assimilate the anesthetic or food, but not both, so it was essential that the patient's period under anesthesia be as short as possible. And while the limb replacements were relatively simple microsurgical procedures, removing the damaged organ from Ten and the healthy one from the deceased Eighteen was going to be tricky and only fractionally less difficult that resiting the donor organ in the receiving patient.

The organs of absorption of the physiological classification FROB were unique among the warm-blooded oxygen-breathing life-forms known to the Galactic Federation—even though, properly speaking, the Hudlars did not breathe. Situated under the skin of each flank, the organs were large semicircular and extraordinarily complex structures covering more than one-sixth of the body area and separated along their upper edges by the spinal column. The organs were integral with the skin, which was pitted in those areas by several thousands of tiny slits whose opening and closure was controlled by a network of voluntary muscles, and extended deeply into the body to a depth which varied between nine and sixteen inches.

Serving as it did the functions of both stomach and lungs, the combination of nutrition and air which was the dense, souplike atmosphere of Hudlar was taken in by the two large organs, and in a remarkably short period of time, the usable content of the gaseous liquid and solid mixture was abstracted and the residue passed into a single smaller and biologically less complex organ sited on the underside where the wastes were evacuated as a milky liquid.

The two hearts, situated in tandem between the organs

of absorption and protected by the central vertebrae, circulated the blood at a rate and pressure which had made the early attempts at Hudlar surgery extremely hazardous for the patients. Now, however, much FROB surgical experience had been amassed since the planet's inception into the Federation, and what was more important, a Hudlar was very hard to kill.

Unless, as in this case, it was more than half-dead already.

The team's one big advantage was that all of the procedures, the multiple replacements of limbs and organs of absorption, would be open surgery. There would be no delving and cutting and suturing in tiny, restricted interorgan spaces. More than one surgeon could enter the operative field when required, and Conway knew with certainty that the operating frame around FROB-Ten would shortly be the busiest place in the hospital.

Edanelt was giving final directions regarding the presentation of the patient to its nurses when Conway left to visit FROB-Forty-three. He was beginning to feel that he was in the way again, a feeling to which he had become increasingly accustomed as his growing seniority in recent years had necessitated greater delegation of authority and responsibility. But he knew that Edanelt, as one of the hospital's foremost Senior Physicians, was itself too responsible a doctor to hesitate about calling for Conway's assistance should it get into trouble.

A superficial examination of FROB-Forty-three would have suggested that there was not very much wrong with the patient. All six of the limbs were present and clearly in an undamaged condition, the porous tegument covering its organs of absorption was intact, and it was apparent that the cranial casing and spine had retained their structural integrity in spite of this particular Hudlar having been in a section of the wrecked accommodation module which had sustained the heaviest casualties. The case notes made brief mention of the fact that it had been shielded by the body of another FROB who had little chance of survival.

But the sacrifice on the part of Forty-three's companion—in all probability its life-mate—could have been wasted. Just inside the midlimb on the right underside there was a pressure cap and temporary dressing which concealed the opening of a deep, punctured wound made by a length of bar metal which had penetrated the tegument like a blunt spear. It had torn the side of the womb—the patient had been in Hudlar female mode at the time of the accident—and while it had missed the major blood vessels in the area, it had stopped within a fraction of an inch of the rearmost heart.

The fetus seemed to be in good condition in spite of the metal bar having passed within a few inches of its spine. While the heart itself had not been damaged, the blunt end of the metal bar had pinched off the circulation to the heart muscles on that side to the point where irreversible deterioration had taken place. Cardiac activity was being maintained by the life-support system, but even with that assistance the heart was in imminent danger of arrest, and replacement was strongly indicated. Conway sighed, foreseeing yet another emotionally painful post-operative experience for himself.

"A replacement is available from Eighteen," he said to Hossantir, the Tralthan Senior in charge of Forty-three's surgery. "We are already taking its absorption organ and all of its undamaged limbs, so donating a heart as well should not worry it."

Hossantir turned one of its four eyes to regard Conway and said, "Since Eighteen and Forty-three were life-mates, you are almost certainly correct."

"I didn't know that," Conway said uncomfortably, sensing an implied criticism of his flippancy by the Tralthan whose species, unlike the Hudlars, held their recently deceased in high reverence. He went on. "How will you proceed?"

Hossantir's intention was to leave the section of metal bar still present in the wound in place. It had been cut where it passed beneath the skin by the rescuers to facilitate movement of the casualty, but they had wisely not removed the entire bar in case they might complicate the injuries. Since the inner end of the bar was performing a useful function in controlling some of the deeper hemorrhaging, the prior suturing of the tear in the womb would mean that the instruments necessary for the later heart replacement procedure would be able to pass it without risk of endangering the fetus.

The external wound was not in the position Hossantir would have chosen for a heart replacement operation, but it was close enough for the purpose following surgical enlargement—a course which would avoid subjecting the patient to the additional trauma of another deep incision.

When the Tralthan had finished speaking, Conway looked around the operating frame and at the surgical team drifting weightlessly nearby. There was a Melfan, two Orligians, and another Tralthan who were all junior surgeons, and five Kelgian and two Ian nurses, all of whom were watching him silently. He knew that Senior Physicians could be very touchy about seeming infringements of their authority, and especially when they were ordered to do something as a result of a simple omission on their own part. His Kelgian alter ego wanted him to come straight to the point, while the Tralthan component of his mind advised a more diplomatic approach.

"Even with surgical enlargement of the wound," he said carefully, "access to the operative field will be restricted."

"Naturally," Hossantir replied. Conway tried a more direct approach.

"No more than two surgeons will be able to operate at any given time," he went on, "so there will be a high degree of team redundancy."

"Of course," Hossantir said.

"Senior Physician Edanelt," Conway said firmly, "needs help."

Two of Hossantir's eyes curled around to regard the preparations going on around Edanelt's frame, then it quickly detailed his two Orligian and the Tralthan medics to help the other Senior with instructions to call on whatever nursing support as and when needed.

"That was unforgivably selfish and thoughtless of me," Hossantir went on to Conway. "I thank you for the tactful way in which you reminded me of the transgression in the presence of my subordinates. But please be more direct in future. I carry permanently a Kelgian Educator tape and will not take offense over any seeming infringement of my authority. Frankly, I am greatly reassured by your presence, Conway, since my experience of deep Hudlar surgery is not extensive."

If I were to detail my own experience of Hudlar surgery, Conway thought wryly, *you might not feel reassured at all.*

Then he smiled suddenly, remembered how O'Mara had sardonically described the function of a Diagnostician in an operating theater as being largely psychological—the being was there principally to worry and accept the responsibilities its subordinates might not be able to carry.

As he moved between the three patients, Conway recalled his first few years after promotion to Senior Physician and of how he had accepted, and at times jealously guarded, his responsibilities. While working under supervision he had attempted to show that the Diagnostician concerned was redundant. In time he had been successful, because the supervision had become minimal and at times nonexistent. But there had also been a few times when Thornnastor or one of the other Diagnosticians who had been breathing down his neck and causing an irritating distraction during surgery had stepped in and saved a patient's life as well as the professional career of a very new Senior Physician whose enthusiasm verged on the irresponsible.

How those Diagnosticians had been able to watch without intervening, or suggesting alternative procedures, or giving step-by-step instructions at every stage, Conway did not know, because he himself was finding it just barely possible to do so.

He managed to continue doing the near-impossible while the hours slid past, dividing his attention between the operating stations of Yarrence, Edanelt, and Hossantir as well as the activity around the deceased Eighteen, where the surgery required to withdraw the donor organs and limbs was as painstaking and precise as that being performed on the recipients. There were several aspects of the work he could have commented upon, although not in overly critical terms, so he remained silent and gave advice only when it was requested. But while the three Seniors were doing very well and he was careful to divide his time equally among them, the one he watched most carefully was Hossantir. If any of the patients were going to cause problems, it would be FROB-Forty-three.

It happened in the fifth hour of the operations. The depressed cranial fracture and arterial repair on Three had gone well, and the less critical work of limb replacement was proceeding in satisfactory fashion. On FROB-Ten the absorption organ replacement work was completed and the decompression damage had been repaired so that it, too, had only the time-consuming microsurgical work on the limbs to undergo. It was natural, therefore, for Conway to hook himself to Forty-three's frame to watch Hossantir performing the highly delicate initial stages of reconnecting the replacement heart.

There was a sudden, silent explosion of Hudlar blood.

Chapter 15

HOSSANTIR made a sound which did not translate, and its manipulators holding the long-handled instruments moved with incredible slowness as they felt about in the totally obscured operative field. Its assistant, also moving with a lack of urgency which could only have been subjective to Conway's racing mind, introduced a clamp but could not find the vessel which was hemorrhaging. Trained as he was to react quickly and positively to such emergencies, Conway did not move slowly.

He could not move at all.

His hands, his stupid five-fingered, Earth-human, and utterly alien hands, trembled uncontrollably while his multiple mind tried desperately to decide what to do with them.

He knew that this kind of thing could happen to medics who were carrying too many tapes, but that it should not happen too often if the doctor concerned hoped to make it as a Diagnostician. Frantically, he tried to impose order on the warring factions within his mind by calling up the memory of O'Mara, who was totally unsympathetic where disorderly thinkers were concerned—in particular, the memory of the Chief Psychologist telling him what the Educator tapes were and, more importantly, what they were not.

No matter how he felt subjectively, his mind was *not* being taken over by the alien personalities who were apparently sharing it—his Earth-human mind had simply been given a large quantity of extraterrestrial knowledge on which it could draw. But it was very difficult to convince himself of that when the other-species material in his mind belonged to medical people with their own individual ideas on how he should react to this emergency.

The ideas were very good, particularly those of the Melfan and Tralthan components. But they required the use of ELNT pincers or FGLI primary manipulators, not Earth-human fingers, and he was being urged to do too many things at once with the wrong organic equipment.

Hossantir's Melfan assistant whose ID, like everything else in the immediate area, was obscured by the bloody spray, said urgently, "I can't see. My visor is—"

One of the nurses quickly cleaned the helmet in front of the eyes, not wasting time on the rest of the transparent bubble. But the fine red spray was re-covering it as Conway watched. And that was not the only problem, because, deep inside the operative field, the light sources on the instruments were likewise obscured.

The Tralthan Senior had been closest so that only the front of its bubble helmet had been affected. One of its eyes curled back to regard Conway through the still transparent rear section.

"We require assistance, Conway. Can you suggest a . . ." Hossantir began; then it noticed the trembling hands and added, "Are you indisposed?"

Conway clenched his fists slowly—everything seemed to be happening in the slowest of slow motion—and said, "It is temporary."

Silently he added, *I hope.*

But the alien personalities who were not really there were still clamoring for attention. He tried to ignore all but one of them at a time, thinking vaguely of the principle of divide and rule, but that did not work either. All of them were offering medical or surgical advice, all of it had potential value in the present situation, and all of it called for an immediate response. The only available material which did not force itself forward was the Gogleskan data accidentally provided by Khone, and that was of little value anyway. But for some reason his mind kept returning to it, holding on to that frightened but strong-willed alien personality as if it were some kind of psychological life-raft.

Khone's presence was not at all like the sharp, intense, and artifically enhanced impressions produced by the Educator tapes. He found himself concentrating on the little being's mental imprint, even though the strange and visually terrifying creatures around the operating frame threatened to throw it into a panic reaction. But the Gogleskan data also included material on Conway's work at the hospital, transferred to its mind during the mishap on Goglesk, and this to a certain extent had prepared Khone for just this kind of experience. It was also a member of a race of individualists whose mental processes were adept at avoiding contact with, or of negating the influence of, other beings around them.

More than any other entity in Conway's experience, Khone knew how to ignore people.

All at once his hands were no longer shaking and the alien bable within his mind had quieted to an insistent murmur which he could choose to ignore. He tapped the Melfan assisting Hossantir sharply on its carapace.

"Please withdraw and leave your instruments in position," he said. To the Tralthan Senior he added, "The bleeding is obscuring everything in the operative field, including the magnifiers and light sources of the instruments and, if we approach closely, our visors. We must . . ."

"Suction isn't working, Conway," Hossantir broke in, "and won't until the flow has been checked at source. But we can't see the source!"

". . . Use the scanners," Conway continued quietly, enclosing the tiny, hollow-coned handles of the Melfan clamp with his Earth-human fingers, "in conjunction with my hands and your eyes."

Since normal vision was useless because of his helmet's close proximity to the spray from the wound, Conway's idea was that Hossantir use two scanners angled so as to bear on the operative field from two viewpoints as far apart as possible. This would give an accurate stereoscopic picture of what was happening which the Senior could describe for him and guide the movements of his clamp. He would be operating blind, but only long enough to find and seal off the bleeder, after which the operation would proceed in the normal way. It would be a very uncomfortable few minutes for Hossantir, two of whose four eyes would be extended laterally to the limits of its flattened, ovoid helmet. It would also have to withdraw temporarily from the operation, Conway told it apologetically, so that its scanners and helmet would not be affected by the spray.

"This could give me a permanent squint," Hossantir said, "but no matter."

None of his alter egos saw anything funny in the idea of a great, elephantine Tralthan with a squint in two of its widely extensible eyes. Fortunately, a smothered Earth-human laugh was not translatable.

His hands and the instruments felt heavy and awkward, and not just because he was using Melfan clamps. The gravity nullification field surrounding him did not, of necessity, extend to the patient, so that everything at the operating site weighed four times heavier than normal. But the Tralthan used its scanners to guide him verbally to the blood vessel which had to be origin of the massive hemorrhaging, and considering the elevated blood pressure of the Hudlar life-form, he expected to feel resistance as he clamped it off.

There was none, and the bleeding continued with undiminished force.

One of his alter egos had encountered something like this situation during a transplant on an entirely different life-form, a diminutive Nidian whose blood pressure had been only a fraction of that of this Hudlar. On that occasion the blood flow had also been a fine spray rather than the pulsing stream characteristic of arterial bleeding, and the trouble had been due to a mechanical failure rather than to faulty surgical technique.

Conway was not sure if that was the problem here, but a part of his multiple mind felt sure, and he decided to trust that part.

"Stop the artificial heart," he said firmly. "Cut off the blood supply to the area."

"We can easily make good the blood loss," Hossantir objected, "but cutting off circulation for more than a few minutes could kill the patient."

"Do it now," Conway said.

Within a few seconds the bright red spray had subsided and died. A nurse cleaned Conway's visor while Hossantir used suction to clear the operative field. They did not need the scanners to see what had happened.

"Technician, quickly," Conway said.

Before he had finished speaking there was a furry little Nidian, looking like a gift-wrapped teddy bear in its transparent OR suit, hovering beside his elbow.

"The nonreturn valve of the connector is jammed in the closed position," the Nidian said in its staccato, barking speech. "This was caused, I would say, by the valve setting being altered accidentally when it was struck by one of the surgical instruments. The flow from the artificial heart has been blocked and was forcing its way out via the recess of the valve setting control, hence the fine, high-pressure spray. The valve itself isn't damaged, and if you will raise the organ so that I will have space to reset the valve..."

"I'd rather not move the heart," Conway said. "We are very short of time."

"I am not a doctor," the Nidian said crossly. "This repair should properly be performed on a workbench, or at least in an area with room for my admittedly small elbows. Working in close contact with living tissue is . . . is repugnant to me. However, my tools are sterile in readiness for such emergencies."

"Do you feel nauseous?" Conway asked worriedly. He had visions of the little being choking inside its helmet.

"No," the Nidian said, "just irritated."

Conway withdrew his Melfan instruments to give the technician more room to work. A nurse had clipped a tray of Earth-human DBDG instruments to the frame beside him, and by the time he had selected the ones he would need the Nidian had freed the jammed valve. Conway was thanking the little being for the speed of the repair when Hossantir broke in.

"I'm restarting the artificial heart," it said.

"No, wait," Conway said sharply. He was looking at the monitor and getting a feeling—a very vague feeling that was not strong enough even to be called a hunch—that any delay at all would be dangerous. "I don't like the vital signs. There is nothing there which should not be there, considering that the flow from the artificial heart was interrupted, initially by the jammed connector valve and later when the system was shut down during the repair. I realize that if the artificial heart is not restarted within the next few minutes, irreversible changes leading to termination will take place in the brain. Even so, I have the feeling that we should not restart but go instead for an immediate resection of the replacement organ . . ."

He knew that Hossantir would want to object and take the safer course, that of restarting the artificial heart and waiting until they were sure that the patient's circulation had returned to optimum, and then proceed as originally planned. Normally Conway would not have argued against this, because he, too, preferred not to take unnecessary risks. But there was something niggling at the back of his mind, or one of his minds, something about the effect of long-term trauma on certain gravid, heavy-gravity life-forms, and the feeling was so persistent that he had to act on it. And while he had been speaking, Conway had unclipped his instruments to show Hossantir, nonverbally so that the Senior's feelings would not be hurt too much, that he was not about to argue the point.

". . . Will you work on the connection to the absorption organ, please," he ended, "and keep an eye on the monitor."

Sharing the operative field with the Tralthan, Conway worked quickly and carefully in the restricted space, clamping off the artery beyond the artificial heart connection, detaching it, and reconnecting it to the arterial stub projecting from the replacement organ. Unlike the first, shocking seconds of the earlier hemorrhaging, time seemed to have speeded up. His hands and instruments were well outside the field of the nullifiers, being acted on by four Earth-Gs, so they felt incredibly slow and awkward. Several times his instruments clinked loudly against those of Hossantir. He could sympathize with the surgeon, whoever it had been, who had accidentally knocked that connector valve off its setting. He had to concentrate hard to keep his instruments from leading a life of their own.

He did not watch Hossantir's work, because the Tralthan knew its stuff and there was no time for surgical sightseeing.

He inserted retaining sutures to hold the artery in position on each end of the connector, which was designed both to hold the ends firmly in position when circulation was restored and to keep the sections of original and replacement tissue apart so as to reduce postoperative rejection problems. There were times when, immunologically speaking, he wondered why a highly evolved and complex organism should be its own worst enemy. Next he began the linkup of the vessel which supplied nutrient from the absorption organ to one of the major heart muscles.

Hossantir had completed its connection and had turned its attention to the minor vessel which supplied one half of the womb when the Hudlar was in female mode—the second, undamaged heart had been performing double duty since the start of the operation. They were short of time, but as yet not dangerously so, when the Tralthan indicated the Monitor with a free appendage.

"Ectopics," Hossantir said. "One in five, no, one in four. Pressure is reducing. The indications are that the heart will go into fibrillation and arrest very quickly. The defibrillator is ready."

Conway took a quick look at the visual display where the irregular, ectopic heartbeat broke into the normal rhythm once in every four beats. From experience he knew how soon it could degenerate into a rapid, uncontrollable flutter and, with the subsequent loss of the pumping function, failure. The defibrillator would almost certainly shock it into action again, but that device could not be used while the operation on the replacement heart was in progress. He resumed his work with desperate, careful speed.

So deep was his concentration that all of his minds were becoming involved again, contributing their expertise and at the same time their irritation that it was a set of Earth-human hands which were doing the work and not the assorted manipulators, pincers, and digits of his alter egos. He looked up finally to find that Hossantir and he had finished their connections at the same time. But a few seconds later the other heart went into fibrillation, then arrest. Their time was really short now.

They eased the clamps on the main artery and secondary vessels and watched the flaccid replacement organ swell slowly as it was filled with Forty-three's blood, checking with their scanners for the formation of air embolisms. There were none, so Conway placed the four tiny electrodes in position preparatory to restarting the replacement heart. Unlike the defibrillator charge needed for the other heart, which would have to penetrate more than ten inches of hard, Hudlar tegument and underlying tissue, these electrodes would be acting directly on the surface muscles of the replacement organ and would be carrying a relatively mild charge.

The defibrillator brought negative results. Both hearts fluttered unsteadily for a few moments and then subsided.

"Again," Conway said.

"The embryo has arrested," Hossantir said suddenly.

"I was expecting that," Conway said, not wanting to sound omniscient, but neither did he have the time for explanations.

Now he knew why he had wanted to complete the replacement connections so fast after the emergency with the valve. It had been not a hunch but a memory from the past when he had been a very junior intern, and the memory was one of his own.

It had happened during his first lecture on the FROB life-form, which had been given by the Diagnostician-in-Charge of Pathology, Thornnastor. Conway had made a remark to the effect that the species was fortunate in having a standby heart if one should fail. Conway had meant it as a joke, but Thornnastor had jumped on him, figuratively speaking, with all six of its feet for making such a remark without first studying the Hudlar physiology in detail. It had gone on to describe the disadvantages of possessing two hearts, especially when the possessor was a gravid female-mode Hudlar nearing parturition, and the nerve network which controlled the involuntary muscle system was maintaining a delicate balance between the impulses to four hearts, two parental and two embryonic. At that particular stage the failure of one heart could quickly lead to the arrest of the other three.

"And again," Conway said worriedly. The incident had not been worth remembering then, because major surgery on FROBs was considered to be impossible in those days. He was wondering if survival for this particular Hudlar was impossible now when both of its hearts twitched, hesitated, then settled into a strong, steady beat.

"The fetal hearts are picking up," Hossantir said. A few second later it added, "Pulse-rate optimal."

On the sensor screen the cerebral traces were showing normal for a deeply unconscious Hudlar, indicating that there had been no brain dămage as a result of the few minutes cessation of circulation, and Conway began to relax. But oddly, now that the emergency was over the other occupants of his mind were becoming uncomfortably obtrusive. It was as if they, too, were relieved and were reacting with too much enthusiasm to the situation. He shook his head irritably, telling himself once again that they were only recordings, simply stored masses of information and experience which were available to his, Conway's, mind to use or ignore as he saw fit. But then the uncomfortable thought came to him that his own mind was simply a collection of knowledge, impressions, and experience collected over his lifetime, and what made his mind data so much more important and significant than that of the others?

He tried to ignore that suddenly frightening thought by reminding himself that he was still alive and capable of receiving new impressions and continuously modifying his total experience as a result of them, while the taped material had been frozen at the time it had been donated. In any case, the donors were long since deceased or far removed from Sector General. But Conway's mind felt as though it was beginning to doubt its own authority, and he was suddenly afraid for his sanity.

O'Mara would be furious if he knew Conway was indulging in this kind of thinking. So far as the Chief Psychologist was concerned, a doctor was responsible for his work and for the tools, both physical and psychological, which enabled him to do that work. If the doctor could not perform satisfactorily, then the person concerned should seek a less demanding job.

There were few jobs more demanding than that of a Diagnostician.

His hands were beginning to feel wrong again, and the fat, pink, and strangely awkward fingers were trembling. Conway stowed away his DBDG instruments and turned to Hossantir's Melfan assistant, whose ID was still smeared with blood and only partly readable, and said, "Would you like to resume, Doctor?"

"Thank you, sir," the ELNT said. Obviously it had been worrying in case Conway, as a result of his intervention, had thought the Melfan incapable of doing the work. *Right now*, he thought grimly, *the opposite is true*.

"It is not expected," Hossantir said gravely, "that you should do everything yourself, Conway."

Plainly the Tralthan knew that something was wrong with him—Hossantir's eyes missed nothing, even when all four of them seemed to be looking in other directions. Conway watched for a few minutes until the team had closed up, then he left Forty-three to check on the progress of the other two patients. Psychologically he felt unwell.

The organ of absorption had been successfully transplanted into Ten, and Edanelt and his team were busy with the microsurgery required on the replacement limbs. The patient was out of danger, however, because the new organ had been tested with an application of nutrient paint and the sensors showed that it was performing satisfactorily. While he was complimenting the team on its work, Conway stared at the heavy staples which held the edges of the wound together—so closely sutured were they that the wound looked like an enormous zip-fastener. But nothing less would serve to hold an FROB's hard, thick, and incredibly tough hide together, and the material of the staples was molecularly unstable so that they could be rendered flexible for withdrawal when the healing process was complete.

But an almost invisible scar, the Hudlar component of Conway's mind insisted, would be the least of this patient's problems.

All at once Conway wanted to run away from all this major surgery and its attendant postoperative problems, instead of having to make yet another examination of a third Hudlar patient.

Yarrence had concentrated its efforts on the cranial injury, leaving FROB-Three's abdominal wound to the medics freed by the demise of FROB-Eighteen, while the remaining members of both teams were deployed on the limb amputation and replacement work. It was obvious after the first few minutes that they were engaged in performing a very complex but smooth-running operation.

From the talk around the frame he gathered that it was also an operation without precedent. To Conway it had seemed to be an obvious solution to FROB-Three's problem, replacing the missing forelimbs with two from the rear. While not as precise as the originals they would be much more satisfactory in every way than the prosthetics, and there would be no rejection problems. He had read in the old medical texts of Earth-human arm amputees learning to draw, write, and even eat with their feet, and the Hudlar feet were much more adaptable than those of an Earth-human DBDG. But the admiration that simple solution had aroused among the team was making Conway feel embarrassed, because, given the present circumstances, anyone could have thought of it.

It was the circumstances which were without precedent—the Menelden disaster with its aftermath of massively injured Hudlars requiring transplant surgery together with the ready availability of spare parts. The possibility of one of the transplant cases being able to return to its home planet with the bonus of a pair of forelimbs which were almost as good as the originals was an idea which would have occurred to any moral coward like himself, who dreaded those postop conversations with patients whose transplants were from normal donors rather than from themselves.

Conway made a mental note to separate FROB-Three from Ten and Forty-three before they returned to consciousness and could begin talking together. The atmosphere between Three and its two less fortunate colleagues would be strained to say the least, and their convalescence would be difficult enough without two of the three being eaten up with envy.

Consideration of the FROB's problems had brought his Hudlar component into prominence again, and it was difficult not to sympathize and suffer at the thought of his patient's postoperative life-style. He tried to bring forward the material on the Tralthan, Melfan, and Kelgian components who, as other-species medics, should have been more clinical regarding the situation. But they, too, were overly sympathetic and their responses painful. In desperation he called up the material of Khone, the Gogleskan, who retained its sanity and intelligence by isolating itself from all close contacts with its fellows.

The Gogleskan material was not at all like that of an ordinary Educator tape. It had more texture, more immediacy, as if another person were truly sharing his mind, however reluctantly. With this degree of understanding between them, he wondered how it would feel to meet and talk to Khone again.

It was unlikely to happen in the hospital, Conway was sure, because the experience of staying in Sector General would probably drive Khóne insane, and O'Mara would never allow it anyway. One of the Chief Psychologist's strictest rules was that tape donors and carriers must never be allowed to meet because of the psychòlogical trauma, incalculable in its intensity, which would result if two entities of widely different species, but possessing identical personalities, tried to communicate.

In the light of what had happened to Conway on Goglesk, O'Mara might have to modify that rule.

And now even the problems of the Gogleskans were clamoring for Conway's attention, as were the Tralthan, Kelgian, Melfan, and Illensan occupants of his mind. Conway moved back to a position where he could watch the activity around all three operating frames without the team-members being able to see his distress. But the alien babel in his mind was so bad that he could scarcely speak, and it was only with a great effort that he could comment on some aspect of the work or give a wòrd of praise to one of the medics. All at once he wanted out, and to escape from his too-demanding selves.

With a tremendous effort he guided his alien fingers to the transmit key for his general communication and said carefully, "You people are too good and there is nothing here for me to do. If a problem should arise, call me on the Red Three frequency. There is a matter which I must attend to at once on the methane level."

As he was leaving, Hossantir bent an eye-stalk in his direction and said gravely, "Stay cool, Conway."

Chapter 16

THE ward was cold and dark. Heavy shielding and insulation protected it against the radiation and heat given off by the ship traffic in the vicinity of the hospital, and there were no windows, because even the light which filtered in from the distant stars could not be allowed to penetrate to this level. For this reason the images appearing on his vehicle's screen had been converted from the nonvisible spectrum which gave the pictures the unreal quality of fantasy, and the scales covering Diagnostician Semlic's eight-limbed, starfish-shaped body shone coldly through the methane mist like multihued diamonds, making it resemble some wondrous, heraldic beast.

Conway had often studied pictures and scanner records of the SNLU life-form, but this was the first time he had seen Semlic outside its refrigerated life-support vehicle. In spite of the proven efficiency of Conway's own insulated vehicle, the Diagnostician was keeping its distance.

"I come in response to your recent invitation," Conway said hesitantly, "and to escape from that madhouse up their for a while. I have no intention of examining any of your patients."

"Oh, Conway, it's you inside that thing!" Semlic moved fractionally closer. "My patients will be greatly relieved by your lack of attention. That furnace you insist on occupying makes them nervous. But if you would park to the right of the observation gallery, just there, you will be able to see and hear everything that goes on. Have you been here before?"

"Twice," Conway replied. "Purely to satisfy my curiosity on both occasions, as well as to enjoy the peace and quiet."

Semlic made a sound which did not translate, then said, "Peace and quiet are relative, Conway. You have to turn the sensitivity of your outside microphone right up to hear me with sufficient volume for your translator to be able to handle my input, and I am speaking loudly for an SNLU. To a being like you, who are nearly deaf, it is quiet. I hope that the environment, busy and noisy as it is to me, will help bring the peace and calm which your mind requires so badly.

"And don't forget," it said as it moved away, "turn your sound sensitivity up and your translator off."

"Thank you," Conway said. For a moment the jeweled starfish shape of the Diagnostician aroused in him an almost childlike sense of wonder, so that a sudden wave of emotion misted his eyes and added to the blurring effect of the methane fog filling the ward as he added, "You are a kind, understanding, and warmhearted being."

Semlic made another untranslatable sound and said, "There is no need to be insulting..."

For a long time he watched the activity in the busy ward and noticed that a few of the low-temperature nursing staff attending the patients wore lightweight protective suits, indicating that their atmosphere requirements were somewhat different from the ward in general. He saw them doing things to and for their charges which made no sense at all, unless he was to take an SNLU tape, and they worked in the almost total silence of beings with a hypersensitivity to audible vibrations, and at first there was nothing to hear. But the more deeply he concentrated the more aware he became of delicate patterns of sound emerging, of a kind of alien music which was cold and pure and resembled nothing he had ever heard before, and eventually he could distinguish single voices and conversations which were like the cool, passionless, delicate, and ineffably sweet chiming of colliding snowflakes. Gradually the peace and beauty and utter strangeness of it all reached him and the other components of his mind, and gently dissolved away all the stress and conflict and mental confusion.

Even Khone, in whom xenophobia was an evolutionary imperative, could find nothing threatening in these surroundings, and it, too, found the peace and calm which enables the mind either to float without thinking or to think clearly and coolly and without worrying.

Except, that was, for a small, niggling worry over the fact that he had been here for several hours while there was important work awaiting his attention, and besides which, it had been nearly ten hours since he had eaten.

The cold level had served its purpose very well by leaving him in all respects cool. Conway looked around for Semlic, but the SNLU had disappeared into a side ward. He turned on his translator, meaning to ask two nearby patients to pass on his message of thanks to the Diagnostician, but hastily changed his mind.

The delicate chiming and tinkling speech of the two SNLU patients translated as "... Nothing but a whining, hypochondriac cow! If it wasn't such a kindly being, it would tell you so and probably kick you out of the hospital. And the shameless way you try to get its sympathy is not far short of seduction ..." and, in reply, "You have nothing to be seductive with, you jealous old bitch! You're falling apart. But it still knows which one of us is really ill, even when I try to hide it ..."

As he left Conway made a mental note to ask O'Mara what the ultrafrigid SNLUs did about cooling a situation which had become emotionally overheated. And what, for that matter, could he do to calm down the perpetually pregnant Protector of the Unborn he would be calling on as soon as he had something to eat. But he had the feeling that the answer would be the same in both cases, nothing at all.

When he had returned to the normal warmth and light of the interlevel corridors, he stopped to think.

The distance between his present position and the level

occupied by the Protector was roughly the same as that to the main dining hall which lay in the opposite direction, which meant that he would have a double journey no matter which area he visited first. But his own quarters were between him and the Protector, and Murchison always liked to have food available—a habit dating back to her nursing days—in case a sudden emergency or sheer fatigue kept her from visiting the dining hall. The menu was not varied, but then all he wanted to do was refuel.

There was another reason for avoiding the dining hall. In spite of the fact that his limbs no longer seemed quite so foreign to him, and the people passing him in the corridor were not nearly so unsettling as they had been before his visit to Semlic's wards, and he felt in control of his alter egos, he was not sure that he could remain so if he were to be exposed to the proximity of masses of food which his taped entities might find nauseating.

It would not look good if he had to pay another visit to Semlic so soon. He did not think that the type of cold comfort he had received was habit-forming, but the law of diminishing returns would most certainly apply.

When he arrived Murchison was dressed, technically awake, but in a powered-down condition, and about to go on duty. They both knew, and they were careful not to mention to each other that they knew, that O'Mara had arranged their free periods to coincide as seldom as possible—the assumption being that it was sometimes better to put off a problem rather than cause unnecessary grief by trying to solve it too soon. Murchison yawned at him and wanted to know what he had been doing and what, apart from sleeping, he intended doing next.

"Food, first," Conway said, yawning in sympathy. "Then I have to check on the condition of the FSOJ. You remember that Protector? You were in at its birth."

She remembered it, all right, and said so in terms which were less than ladylike.

"How long is it since you've had any sleep?" she went on, trying to hide her concern by pretending to be cross. "You look worse than some of the patients in intensive care. Your taped entities will not feel fatigue, because they weren't tired when they donated their brain recordings, but don't let that fool you into thinking that you are tireless."

Conway fought back another yawn, then reached forward suddenly to grab her around the waist. He was pretty sure that his arms were not trembling as he held her, even though his arousal was being matched by equivalent feelings in his alter egos, but the kiss was much less lingering than was usual. Murchison pushed him away gently.

"Do you have to go right away?" he asked, fighting another mammoth yawn.

Murchison laughed. "I'm not going to fool about with you in that condition. You'd probably arrest. Go to bed before you go to sleep. I'll fix you something before I leave, something hidden inside a sandwich so that your mind-friends won't object to what you're eating."

As she busied herself at their food dispenser, she went on, "Thorny is very interested in the birth process in the Protector, and it has asked me to check the patient at frequent intervals. I'll call you if anything unusual develops there, and I'm sure the Seniors in Hudlar OR will do the same."

"I really ought to check them myself," Conway said.

"What's the use of having assistants," she said impatiently, "if you insist on doing all the work yourself?"

Conway, with the remains of his first sandwich in one hand and an unspecified but no doubt nutritious cup of something in the other, sat down on their bed. He said, "Your argument is not without merit."

She gave him an almost sisterly peck on the cheek, a kiss designed to cause minimal arousal in his alter egos as well as his own, and left without another word. O'Mara must have lectured her pretty thoroughly regarding her behavior toward a life-mate who had recently become an acting Diagnostician and who still had to adjust to the attendant emotional confusion.

If he did not adjust soon, he could not look forward to having much fun. The trouble was, Murchison was not giving him much of an opportunity to try.

He awoke suddenly with her hand on his shoulder and

the remains of a nightmare, or it might have been an alien wish-fulfillment dream, dissolving into the comfortable reality of their living quarters.

"You were snoring," she said. "You've probably been snoring for the past six hours. The Hudlar OR and Protector teams left recorded messages for you. They obviously didn't think them urgent or important enough to awaken you, and the rest of the hospital continues to go about its business much as usual. Do you want to go back to sleep?"

"No," Conway said, and reached up to grab her around the waist. Her resistance was a token one.

"I don't think O'Mara would approve of this," she said doubtfully. "He warned me that there would be emotional conflicts, serious enough to permanently affect our relationship, if the process of adaptation is not slow and carefully controlled, and—"

"And O'Mara isn't married to the most pulchritudinous female DBDG in the hospital," Conway broke in, and added, "And since when have I been fast and uncontrolled?"

"O'Mara isn't married to anything but his job," she said, laughing, "and I expect his job would divorce him if it could. But our Chief Psychologist knows his stuff, and I would not want to risk prematurely overstimulating your—"

"Shut up," Conway said softly.

It was possible that the Chief Psychologist was right, Conway thought as he gently rolled her onto the bed beside him; O'Mara usually was right. His alter egos were becoming increasingly aroused, and were looking with other-species disfavor on the features occupying the forward skull and the softly curving mammaries of the Earth-human DBDG in such close proximity to them. And when tactile sensations were added to the visual sensory input, their disfavor became extreme.

They reacted with mental images of what should have been going on in the Hudlar, Tralthan, Kelgian, Melfan, Illensan, and Gogleskan equivalent situation, and they insisted that this was utterly and quite revoltingly *wrong*.

What was worse, they tried to make Conway feel that it was wrong, too, and that the life-mate beside him should have been of an entirely different physiological classification, the exact species being dependent on the emotional intensity of the entity who was protesting the most.

Even the Gogleskan was insisting that this activity was all wrong, but it was disassociating itself from the proceedings. Khone was a rugged individualist, a perfect example of a loner among a species which had evolved to the point where solitude was a prime survival characteristic. And suddenly Conway realized that he was using Khone's Gogleskan presence and ability, that he had already used it on several previous occasions to ignore those thoughts and feelings which had to be ignored and to focus his Earth-human mind on those which required the utmost concentration.

The alien protests were still strong, but the protestors were being put in their places and given a low order of priority. Even the Gogleskan objections were being noted but otherwise ignored. He was using the FOKTs unique ability against itself as well as the others, and Khone's race certainly knew how to concentrate on a subject.

"We shouldn't...be doing...this," Murchison said breathlessly.

Conway ignored her words but concentrated on everything else. There were times when other-species responses to equivalent situations obtruded, insisting that his partner was too large, too tiny, too fragile, the wrong shape, or in the wrong position. But his visual and tactile sensors were those of a male Earth-human, and the stimuli they were receiving overwhelmed the purely mental interference of the others. Sometimes his alter egos suggested certain actions and movements. These he ignored as well, except in a few instances when he was able to modify them to his own purpose. But toward the end all of the alien interference was swamped out, and the hospital's primary reactor could have blown and he would scarcely have noticed it.

When their elevated pulse and respiration rates had returned to something approaching normal, she continued to hold him tightly, not speaking and even more reluctant to let go. Suddenly she laughed softly.

"I was given precise instruction," she said in a tone which contained both puzzlement and relief, "regarding my behavior toward you for the next few weeks or months. The Chief Psychologist said that I should avoid intimate physical contact, maintain a professional and clinical manner during all conversations, and generally consider myself a widow until you had either come to terms with the tapes riding you, or you had been forced to resume your former Senior Physician status. It was an extremely serious matter, I was told, and great amounts of patience and sympathy would be required to see you through this difficult time. I was to consider you a multiple schizophrenic, with the majority of the personalities concerned feeling no emotional bond with me, and in many cases reacting toward me with physical revulsion. But I was to ignore all this because to do otherwise would be to subject you to the risk of permanent psychological damage."

She kissed the tip of his nose and gave a long, gentle sigh. She went on. "Instead I find no evidence of physical revulsion and . . . Well, you don't seem to be entirely your old self. I can't say exactly what the difference is, and I'm not complaining, but you don't appear to be having any psychological difficulties at all and . . . and O'Mara *will* be pleased!"

Conway grinned. "I wasn't trying to please O'Mara . . ." he began, when the communicator beeped urgently at them.

Murchison had set it to record any nonurgent messages so that he could sleep undisturbed, and obviously someone thought his problem urgent enough to wake him. He escaped from her clutches by tickling her under the arms, then directed the communicator's vision pickup away from the devastated bed before answering. It was possible that there was an Earth-human male DBDG at the other end.

Edanelt's angular, chitinous features filled the screen as the Melfan Senior said, "I hope I did not disturb you,

Conway, but Hudlar's Forty-three and Ten have regained consciousness and are pain-free. They are feeling very lucky to be alive and have not yet had time to think about the disadvantages. This would be the best time to talk to them, if you still wish to do so."

"I do," Conway said. He could not think of anything he wanted to do less just then, and the watching Edanelt and Murchison both knew it. He added, "What about Three?"

"Still unconscious but stable," the Senior replied. "I checked its condition a few minutes before calling you. Hossantir and Yarrence left some hours ago to indulge in these periods of physical and mental collapse which you people seem to need at such ridiculously short intervals. I shall speak to Three when it comes to. The problems of adjustment there are not so serious."

Conway nodded. "I'm on my way."

The prospect of what lay ahead of him had brought the Hudlar material rushing in to fill virtually all of his mind, so that his goodbye to Murchison was nonphysical and lacked even verbal warmth. Fortunately, she had come to accept this kind of behavior from him and would ignore it until he was his old self again. As he turned to go, Conway wondered what there was so special about this pink, flabby, ridiculously weak and unbeautiful entity with whom he had spent most of his adult life.

Chapter 17

"YOU have been very fortunate," Conway said, "very fortunate indeed that neither the baby nor you have suffered permanent damage."

Medically that was quite true, Conway told himself. But the Hudlar in his mind thought otherwise, as did the members of the recovery ward staff who had withdrawn to a discreet distance to enable the patient and its physician to talk privately.

"Having said that," Conway went on, "I regret to tell you that you, personally, have not escaped the long-term and perhaps emotionally distressing effects of your injuries."

He knew that he was not being very subtle in his approach, but in many ways the FROB life-form was as direct and forthright as the Kelgians, although much more polite.

"The reason for this is that organ replacement surgery was necessary to keep both of you alive," he continued, appealing to the patient's maternal instincts in the hope that the good news about the young Hudlar would in some measure diminish the misfortune which would shortly befall the older one. "Your offspring will be born without complications, will be healthy, and will be fully capable of leading a normal life on or off its home planet. You, regrettably, will not."

The Hudlar's speaking membrane vibrated with the expected question.

Conway thought for a moment before replying, not wanting to pitch the explanation at too elementary a level. This Hudlar was a mining specialist and highly intelligent;

otherwise it and its life-mate would not have been working the Menelden asteroids. So he told Forty-three that while infant Hudlars sometimes fell seriously ill and a few might even die, adults were never sick, nor were they anything but physically perfect until the advent of senility. The reason for this was that they developed an immunity to their home planet's pathogens which was as complete and perfect as any purely biochemical system could be, and no other species known to Federation medical science could match it. The FROB immune system was such that it would not allow foreign biological material of any kind to attach itself to their bodies without instantly initiating the process of rejection. Fortunately, their superefficient immune system could be neutralized when necessary, and one of these occasions was when vital organs or limbs from a donor were used as surgical replacements.

He had been trying to make the explanation as simple and accurate as possible, but it was apparent that Forty-three's mind was going its own way.

"What about my life-mate?" it said, as if Conway had not been speaking.

Momentarily a mind picture of Eighteen's devastated body took form between the patient and himself, his own medical knowledge combining with that of his Hudlar component to suddenly involve his emotions. He cleared his throat and said, "I am deeply sorry, but your life-mate was so seriously injured that we were unable to maintain life, much less undertake curative surgery."

"It tried to shield us with its body. Did you know that?" the Hudlar said.

Conway nodded sympathetically, then realized that the small movement of an Earth-human head meant nothing to an FROB. His next words were chosen carefully, because he was sure that Forty-three—weakened by the recent major surgery, gravid, close to delivering its offspring, and in its ultimate female mode—would be susceptible to an emotional approach. His Hudlar alter ego was of the opinion that, at worst, some temporary psychological distress might result, while his own experience with other life-forms in similar situations suggested that he might do some good. But the situation was unique so far as this patient was concerned, and he could not be sure of anything.

Of one thing he was very sure. Somehow he had to keep the patient from becoming too deeply introspective regarding its own situation, so that it would be thinking of its unborn rather than itself when the really bad news had to be faced. But the idea of deliberately manipulating the other's emotions in this fashion was making him feel like a very low form of life indeed, somewhere on the level of an Earthly louse.

He wondered why he had not thought of discussing the case with O'Mara before proceeding further—it was potentially serious enough for the Chief Psychologist to be consulted. He might still need to if he made a mess of things now.

"We are all aware," Conway said finally, "of the action of your life-mate in trying to protect you. This type of behavior is common among the members of the more highly intelligent species, especially when the entity concerned is sacrificing itself to save the life of a loved one or a child. In this instance it was able to do both, and what is more, it was instrumental in giving life and unimpaired mobility to two very seriously injured survivors, one of whom is you, who would otherwise have died in spite of its earlier sacrifice."

This time, he thought, *the patient is paying attention.*

"Your life-mate donated its undamaged limbs and one lobe of its nutrient absorption organ to the patient you can see at the other side of the ward," Conway went on. "That patient, like you, will continue to live in a state of perfect physical health, except for some irksome restrictions regarding environment and own-species group activities. And in addition to its protecting you and your unborn child during the accident, you are both continuing to live because one of your hearts was also donated by your life-mate."

"While its presence is gone from you except as a memory," Conway added quietly, "it would not be completely true to say that it had died."

He watched closely to see how Forty-three was taking this blatantly emotional onslaught, but the tegument of the body was too hard and featureless to give any indication of its feelings.

"It tried very hard to keep you alive," he went on, "and so I think you owe it to your life-mate's memory to continue trying very hard to stay alive, although there will be times when this will not be easy."

And now for the bad news, Conway thought.

Gently, he went on to describe the effects of knocking out the FROB immune system—the aseptic environment which the patient would require, the specially prepared and treated food, and the barrier nursing and isolation ward procedures needed to guard against the possibility of any FROB infection invading the body which had been rendered utterly defenseless. Even the infant would have to be removed from the parent immediately after birth. Only visual contact with it would be possible, because the child would be normal in all respects and would therefore be a health hazard to the defenseless parent.

Conway knew that the child would be raised and well cared for on Hudlar—the FROB family and social structures were both highly complex and flexible, and the concept of "orphan" was completely unknown to them. The infant would be deprived of nothing.

"If you yourself were to return to your home world," Conway said in a firmer tone, "the same protective measures would be necessary to keep you alive, and at home your friends would not have the facilities and experience possessed by this hospital. You would be confined to your own quarters, you would have no physical contact with another Hudlar, and the normal range of exercise and work activities would be forbidden. There would also be the constant worry that your protective envelope would be breached or your nutrient infected and, with no natural defense against disease, you would die."

The native Hudlars were not yet medically advanced enough to maintain such a sophisticated facility, so its death would be certain.

The patient had been watching him steadily while he

was speaking. Suddenly its membrane began to vibrate in reply.

"In the situation you describe," it said, "I might not worry too much about dying."

Conway's first inclination was to remind Forty-three of all the work that had gone into keeping it alive, the implication being that it was displaying a lack of gratitude. But the Hudlar component of his mind was making comparisons with the normal FROB life-style and that which Conway was offering it. From the patient's viewpoint he might not have done it a favor, other than by saving the life of its child-to-be. Conway sighed.

"There is an alternative," he said, trying to put some enthusiasm into his tone. "There is a way in which you could lead an active working life, without physical constraints on your movements. In fact, you could travel all over the Federation, return to asteroid mining if you like, or do anything else you have a mind to do so far as your working life is concerned, provided that you do not return to Hudlar."

The patient's membrane vibrated briefly, but the translator was silent. Probably it was a sound of surprise.

Conway had to spend the next few minutes explaining the basic tenets of multispecies medicine to the patient, and how disease and infection was transmissible only among the members of a species with a common evolutionary history and environment. An Ian or a Melfan or a member of any other species would be quite safe with an Earth-human with the most contagious and virulent Earthly diseases, because the victim's pathogens were ineffective against—in fact they would completely ignore and be ignored by—the tissues of any other off-planet species. An ailment could, therefore, only be contracted from a being's own world or people.

"You can see what this means," Conway went on quickly. "After your wounds are healed and the child is born, you will be discharged from the hospital. But instead of confining you to an aseptic prison on your home world and severely restricting your activities, you could elect to go to another planet, where your lack of resistance to

Hudlar diseases would be unimportant, because the pathogens on that world would have no interest in you.

"Your nutrient would be synthesized locally and would not be a source of infection," he continued. "However, immunity suppressant medication will be required periodically to ensure that your immune system does not restart and begin to reject your artificial organs. This will be administered by a medic from the nearest Monitor Corps office, which will be given full instructions regarding your case. The Corps medic will also warn you of impending visits by members of your own species. When this happens you must not go anywhere near them. Do not occupy the same building as they do or, if possible, even the same town."

Unlike the transplant patients of many other species, who could accept donor organs with no rejection problems after a short time on suppressants, the Hudlar immune system had to be permanently neutralized. But this was not the time, Conway thought, to add another misfortune to the list.

"Exchanges of news between you and your friends at home should be by communicator only," Conway went on. "I must stress this point. A visitor of your own species, or even a package sent from home, would harbor the only kind of pathogens capable of infecting and killing you, and they would do so very quickly."

Conway paused to allow the full meaning of his words to sink in. The patient continued to regard him for a long time, its membrane showing no indication of it wanting to speak. This was a Hudlar in full female mode, and its present major concern would be for the safe delivery and future health and happiness of its offspring.

When the birth was successfully accomplished, as it would be, the deceased male-mode life-mate should have been present to take care of the child and to slip gradually into female mode. Because of the death of its partner, that function would be taken over by close relatives. Immediately following the birth, however, this patient would begin the inevitable changeover to full male mode, and in that condition the absence of its life-mate would be particularly distressing.

People of many intelligent species had lost life-mates before now. They had learned to live with it or they had gone out and found another who would accept them. The trouble here was that FROB-Forty-three would not be able to make physical contact with any other member of its species, and would therefore remain in full male mode for the remainder of its life. That, for a young adult Hudlar, would be an intensely frustrating and unhappy condition to be in.

Through the torrent of sex-related Hudlar material which was flooding his mind, a purely Earth-human thought rose to the surface. What would it be like to be forever separated from Murchison and every other member of his species? If he could have Murchison he would not mind having only a bunch of extraterrestrials to talk to and work with—that was the everyday situation at Sector General. But to be cut off from the one form of warm, human, intimate, and mentally as well as physically stimulating contact which he had been taking for granted for so many years—he did not know what he would be able to do about that. The question was unanswerable because the situation was unthinkable.

"I understand," the patient said suddenly, "and thank you, Doctor."

His first thought was to refuse its thanks and instead apologize to it. He had the taped insight which made him in effect another Hudlar, and he wanted to tell how truly sorry he was for subjecting it to the trauma of this highly complex and professionally demanding operation which would give it so many more years of mental suffering. But he knew that his mind was oversensitized to the Hudlar material right now, and a doctor should not speak to his patient in such a maudlin and unprofessional fashion.

Instead he said reassuringly, "Your species is very adaptable regarding working environments, and much in demand throughout the Federation on planetary and space projects, and your recovery will be complete. With certain personal restrictions, which will require a high order of mental discipline to negate, your can look forward to leading a very active and useful life."

He did not say a happy life, because he was not that big a liar.

"Thank you, Doctor," the patient said again.

"Please excuse me," Conway said, and escaped.

But not for long. The rapid, irregular tapping of six hard-tipped Melfan legs signaled the approach of Senior Physician Edanelt.

"That was well done, Conway," the Senior said. "A nice blend of clinical fact, sympathy, and encouragement, although you did spend a lot more time with the patient than is usual for a Diagnostician. However, there was a message for you from Thornnastor requesting a meeting as soon and wherever is convenient for you. It did not specify other than saying that it concerned your Protector and that it was urgent."

"If the time and place are of my choice," Conway said slowly, his mind still on the future troubles of FROB-Forty-three, "it can't be too urgent. What about Three and Ten?"

"They, too, are urgently in need of reassurance," Edanelt replied. "Three was the responsibility of Yarrence, who did some delicate and quite brilliant work relieving its depressed cranial fracture and underlying repairs, but no replacement surgery was necessary. Visually, Three will not be an aesthetically pleasing entity to its fellows, but unlike Ten and Forty-three, neither will it be a permanent exile from its home world and people.

"Ten will have the same long-term problems as Forty-three," the Melfan went on. "The procedures for the multiple limb and absorption organ replacements went well, and the prognosis is for a full recovery under the usual strict regimen of suppressants. Since you are short of time, perhaps I should talk to one of them while you speak to the other?

"I am a Senior Physician, Conway," it added, "and not a fledgling Diagnostician like you. But I would not want to keep Thornnastor waiting too long."

"Thank you," Conway said, "and I'll talk to Ten."

Unlike Forty-three, Ten was in male mode and would not be susceptible to emotional manipulation and arguments as the previous patient. He hoped that Thornnastor was being its usual impatient self and not really in a hurry to see him . . .

When it was over he felt in much worse mental shape than the patient, who seemed to have taken the first steps toward the acceptance of its lot without too much emotional distress, probably because it did not have a life-mate. Conway desperately wanted to clear his mind of all things pertaining to the Hudlar life-form, but it was proving extremely difficult to do so.

"Surely it is theoretically possible for two suppressees, living away from their home planet, to meet without endangering each other?" he asked Edanelt when they were out of earshot of the Hudlar patients. "If both had their immune systems suppressed, they should be free of own-species pathogens which would otherwise infect each other. It might be possible to arrange periodic meetings of such exiles which would benefit—"

"A nice, softhearted, and, may I say, softheaded idea," Edanelt broke in. "But if one of these suppressees had an inherited immunity to a pathogen not directly involved with the rejection process, to which the other members of this group had no immunity, they would be in serious danger. But try the idea on Thornnastor, who is the recognized authority on—"

"Thornnastor!" Conway burst out. "I'd forgotten. Has it been? . . ."

"No," Edanelt said. "But O'Mara came in to see if you needed help talking to the replacement patients. It advised me regarding my approach to Three's problems, but said that you did not need help and seemed to be enjoying yourselves too much to be disturbed. Was that a remark denoting approval, or not? From my experience of working among Earth-human DBDGs I assume this was one of those occasions when incorrect verbal data is passed on in the belief that the listener will assume the opposite meaning to be true, but I do not understand this concept you call sarcasm."

"One never knows whether O'Mara is approving or otherwise," Conway said drily, "because he is invariably uncomplimentary and sarcastic."

Nevertheless it gave him a warm fleeing to think that the Chief Psychologist had thought enough of his handling of the postoperative interview with Ten not to interfere. Or maybe he had thought Conway was making such an unholy mess of things that O'Mara was unable, for reasons of discipline, to tell a probationary Diagnostician how abysmally wrong he was in front of junior members of the staff.

But the doubt Conway felt was being swamped by a feeling which was even stronger, a physical need which was being reinforced by the sudden realization that he had had nothing but a sandwich to eat during the past ten hours. He turned quickly to the ward terminal and called up the on- and off-duty rosters of the warm-blooded, oxygen-breathing members of the Senior Staff. He was in luck, their duty rosters coincided.

"Would you contact Thornnastor, please," Conway said as he turned to leave the ward, "and tell it that I will meet it in thirty minutes in the dining hall."

Chapter 18

CONWAY knew the Diagnostician-in-Charge of Pathology well enough to tell it apart from all the other Tralthans using the dining hall, and he was pleasantly surprised to see Murchison at the same table. Thornnastor, as was its wont, was purveying some interspecies gossip to its assistant, and so engrossed in it were they that they did not notice his approach.

"...One would not think it likely or even possible,"

the Tralthan was rumbling pedantically through its translator, "for the urge toward indiscriminate procreative activity to be strong in a life-form which is only a few degrees above absolute zero. But believe me, a fractional elevation in body temperature, even when it is accidentally produced by the treatment, can cause acute embarrassment among the other SNLU genders present. Four genders in one species tends to be confusing anyway, even when one is carrying the SNLU tape, and a certain Melfan Senior, you know who I mean, was sufficiently disturbed emotionally to use its external manipulators to signal its readiness to—"

"Frankly, sir, my trouble is somewhat different..." Murchison began.

"I realize that," Thornnastor replied. "But really, there does not appear to be any great emotional, physical, or psychological problem. Naturally, the mechanics of this particular mating process are distasteful to me personally, but I am willing to consider the matter clinically and give what advice I can."

"My difficulty," Murchison said, "is the distinct feeling I experienced while it was happening that I was being unfaithful five times over."

They're talking about us! Conway thought, feeling his face beginning to redden. But they were still too deeply engrossed to notice either him or his embarrassment.

"I will gladly discuss this matter with my fellow Diagnosticians," Thornnastor resumed ponderously. "Some of them may have encountered similar difficulties. Not myself, of course, because the FGLI species indulges in this activity during a very small proportion of the Tralthan year, and during that period the activity is, well, frenetic and not subject to subtle self-analysis." All of its eyes took on faraway looks for a moment, then it went on. "However, a brief reference to my Earth-human component suggests that you do not concern yourself with minor and unnecessary emotional hairsplitting, and just relax and enjoy the process. In spite of the subtle differences which you mentioned earlier, the process *is* enjoyable?...Oh, hello, Conway."

Thornnastor had raised the eye which had been regarding its food to look at him. It said, "We were just talking about you. You seem to be adapting very well to your multiple tape problems, and now Murchison tells me that—"

"Yes," Conway said quickly. He looked appealingly into the Tralthan's one and Murchison's two eyes and went on. "Please, I would greatly appreciate it if you would not discuss this very personal matter with anyone else."

"I don't see why not," Thornnastor said, bringing another eye to bear on him. "Surely the matter is of intrinsic interest, and would no doubt prove enlightening to colleagues who have faced or are about to face similar problems. Sometimes your reactions are difficult to understand, Conway."

He glared at Murchison, who, he felt, had been far too free in talking about her intrinsically interesting problems with her Chief. But she smiled sweetly back at him, then said to Thornnastor, "You'll have to excuse him, sir. I think he is hungry, and hunger affects his sensorium as well as his blood sugar levels and sometimes makes him behave with a degree of irrationality."

"Ah, yes," the Tralthan said, returning the eye to its plate. "It has the same effect on me."

Murchison was already tapping instructions into the food console for one of his visually noncontroversial sandwiches. He said, "Make it three, please."

He was attacking the first one as Thornnastor, who had the advantage of being able to speak with all four of its mouths, went on. "It seems I must compliment you on the way you are adapting to operative procedures requiring other-species surgical data. Not only were you calling up this data with little or no delay; the indications are that you were initiating new procedures derived from a combination of different entities' experiences. The OR Seniors were most impressed, I have been told."

Chewing furiously, Conway swallowed and said, "It was the Seniors who did all the real work."

"That isn't the way Hossantir and Edanelt tell it,"

Thornnastor said. "But I suppose it is in the nature of things that Seniors do most of the work and the Diagnostician-in-Charge gets most of the credit, or all of the discredit if things go wrong. And speaking of cases which might not go well, I would like to discuss your plans for the birth of your Unborn. The endocrinology of its parent and Protector is quite complex, and I am most interested in this one. However, I can foresee a few purely physical problems which . . ."

Conway nearly choked at the understatement, and it was a moment before he was able to speak.

"Must all verbal communication cease while it is eating?" said Thornnastor impatiently, using the mouth closest to Murchison. "Why wasn't your species foresighted enough to evolve at least one additional orifice for the ingestion of food?"

"Pardon me," Conway said, smiling. "I would be delighted to have any assistance and advice you can give me. The Protectors of the Unborn are the most untreatable life-form we've encountered, and I don't think we have discovered all the problems yet, much less found solutions to them. In fact, I would be most grateful if your commitments would allow you to be present during the birth."

"I thought you'd never ask, Conway," Thornnastor rumbled.

"There are several problems," Conway said, rubbing his middle gently and wondering if one of them was going to be an attack of indigestion through eating his food too quickly. Apologetically, he went on. "But right now my mind is still sensitized to the Hudlar material and the questions which have arisen as a result of my recent experiences in the Hudlar OR and Geriatric wards. The questions are psychological as well as physiological, and so insistent that I find it very difficult to clear my mind for consideration of the Protector case. This is ridiculous!"

"But understandable, considering your recent total involvement with FROB life-forms," Thornnastor said. "But if you have unresolved problems regarding these Hudlars, the simplest way of clearing your mind of this troublesome material is to ask the questions at once and obtain as many answers as possible, even though they may be unsatisfactory or incomplete answers, so that you will have taken the matter as far as it is possible to go with it at the present time. Your mind will accept this and allow you to think of other things, including your perpetually pregnant Protector.

"Your particular mental quirk is far from rare, Conway," the Tralthan went on, slipping into its lecturing voice. "There must be a very good reason why your mind doesn't want to leave the subject. Perhaps it is close to drawing significant conclusions, and if the question is shelved now the pertinent data might fade and be lost. I realize that I am beginning to sound like a psychologist, but one cannot practice medicine without acquiring some knowledge in that field. I can, of course, help you with the physiological questions on the Hudlar life-form, but I suspect that it is the psychological aspect which is crucial. In which case you should consult the Chief Psychologist without delay."

"You mean," Conway said faintly, "call O'Mara right now?"

"Theoretically," the Tralthan replied, "a Diagnostician may request the assistance of any member of the hospital staff at any time, and vice versa."

Conway looked at Murchison, who smiled sympathetically and said, "Call him. On the intercom he can only indulge in verbal violence."

"That," Conway said as he reached for the communicator, "doesn't reassure me at all."

A few seconds later the scowling features of the Chief Psychologist filled the tiny screen, making it impossible to tell how or if he was fully dressed. O'Mara said coldly, "I can tell from the background noise and the fact that you are still masticating that you are calling from the main dining hall. I would point out that I am in the middle of my rest period. I do rest occasionally, you know, just to fool you people into thinking that I'm only human. Presumably there is a good reason for your making this call, or are you complaining about the food?"

Conway opened his mouth, but the combination of facing an angry O'Mara and a mind which was still too busily engaged in formulating his questions kept any words from coming out.

"Conway," O'Mara said with exaggerated patience, "what the blazes do you want?"

"Information," he replied angrily. Then he softened his tone and went on. "I need information which might help in the Hudlar geriatric work. Diagnostician Thornnastor, Pathologist Murchison, and I are presently in consultation regarding..."

"Which means," O'Mara said sourly, "that you've dreamed up some harebrained scheme over lunch."

"...A proposed method of treating their condition," Conway went on. "Regrettably, little can be done for the present occupants of the ward, since the degenerative condition is too far advanced in them. But early preventive treatment might be possible provided my idea has physiological and psychological support. Thornnastor and Murchison can give me detailed information on the former, but the key to their treatment, and any hope of its ultimate success, depends on the behavior under stress, adaptive ability, and potential for reeducation in aged but pregeriatric FROBs. I have not yet discussed the clinical problems which would be encountered, because to do so would be a waste of time if the answers you give me preclude further investigation."

"Go on," O'Mara said, no longer sounding half-asleep.

Conway hesitated, thinking that his period of intensive Hudlar surgery, the visits to the FROB geriatric and infant wards, some old memories from his early childhood, and possibly material from his other-species mind partners had all contributed to an idea which was very likely unworkable, ethically questionable, and so ridiculous that O'Mara might well have second thoughts regarding his suitability as a future Diagnostician. But it was too late now to hold back.

"From my FROB tape and lectures at various times on Hudlar pathology," he went on, nodding in acknowledgment toward Thornnastor, "it is clear that the various painful and incurable conditions to which the aged of that species are prey are traceable to a common cause. The loss of function in the limbs and the abnormal degree of calcification and fissuring at the extremities can be ascribed to the simple deterioration in circulation which is common to the aged of any species.

"This is not a new idea," Conway said, glancing quickly toward Thornnastor and Murchison. "However, as a result of working on a large number of Hudlar limb and organ replacement operations from the Menelden accident, it occurred to me that the deterioration I observed in the organs of absorption and evacuation among the aged FROBs was very similar to the temporary condition which occurred during the replacement of a heart, although at the time I was too busy to note the signs consciously. In short, the problems of the FROB geriatrics are due to circulatory impairment or inadequacy."

"If the idea isn't new," O'Mara said with a flash of his characteristic sarcasm, "why am I listening to it?"

Murchison was watching him in silence. Thornnastor continued to watch its food, Murchison, O'Mara, and Conway, also without speaking.

"The Hudlars are a very energy-hungry species," Conway went on. "They have an extremely high metabolic rate which requires a virtually continuous supply of nutrient via their organs of absorption. The food thus metabolized serves the major organs, such as the two hearts, the absorption organs themselves, the womb when the entity is in gravid female mode, and, of course, the limbs.

"I had learned from the pathology lectures," he continued, "that these six immensely strong limbs are the most energy-hungry system of the body, and demand close to eighty percent of the nutrient metabolized. But it was not until the recent Hudlar experience that my mind was drawn forcibly to this data, and to the fact which is also widely recognized, that it is the ultrahigh metabolic rate and excessive food requirement which enables the adult Hudlar to be so fantastically resistant to injury and disease."

O'Mara was getting ready to interrupt again, and Conway went on quickly. "With the onset of old age their troubles invariably begin in the limbs, which demand an even greater proportion of the body's available resources to fight it. This places increasing stress on the twin hearts, absorption, and evacuation organs, all of which require their share of and are interdependent on the circulatory system's nutrient content. As a result these systems go into partial failure, which further reduces the blood supply to the limbs, and the body as a whole slides into a degenerative spiral."

"Conway," O'Mara said firmly, "I assume this lengthy but no doubt oversimplified clinical picture is for the benefit of the poor, ignorant psychologist so that he will understand the psychological questions when they come, if they ever come."

Continuing with its meal, Thornnastor said, "The clinical picture is oversimplified, I agree, but essentially correct, although your method of describing it suggests a new approach to the problem. I, too, am impatient to know what it is that you intend."

Conway took a deep breath and said, "Very well. It seems to me that the drain on the age-reduced resources of these Hudlars, represented by the irreversible limb conditions, can be alleviated before onset. With reduced stress and a greater share of the available nutrient supply, the hearts and organs of absorption and elimination could maintain their functions for an additional several years while keeping up optimum levels of circulation to the remaining limb or limbs."

All at once it seemed that O'Mara's face in the screen had become a still picture; Murchison was staring at him with a shocked expression, and all four of Thornnastor's eyes had turned to regard him.

"Naturally the procedure would be one of elective surgery," Conway went on, "and would not take place except at the request and the expressed permission of the entity concerned. The surgical problems involved in the removal of four or five limbs are relatively simple. It is the psychological preparation and aftereffects which are paramount and which would determine whether or not the procedure should be tried."

O'Mara exhaled loudly through his nose, then said, "So you want me to tell you if it is possible to sell the pregeriatric Hudlars on the idea of voluntary multiple limb amputations?"

"The procedure," Thornnastor said, "does seem, well, radical."

"I realize that," Conway said. "But from the Hudlar material available to me it is obvious that there is a general and abject fear of growing old among that species, caused by the quite appalling clinical picture of the average geriatric FROB. The fear is increased by the knowledge that the minds of the aging Hudlars remain clear and active, although there is the tendency common to all aging entities to want to live in the past. But it is the situation of a normal mind being trapped inside a rapidly degenerating and often pain-racked body which causes the greatest distress. It is possible that the Hudlars may not have a lot of sales resistance to the idea, and may even welcome it.

"But my information is purely subjective," he went on, "and comes from recent personal experience and from the feelings of the Hudlar who donated my tape, so my thinking may not be completely trustworthy. It requires the objective viewpoint of a psychologist with extraterrestrial experience, including that of the FROB life-form, to decide whether or not my idea has merit."

O'Mara was silent for a long time; then he nodded and said, "What can you offer these close-to-limbless Hudlars, Conway? What could they do which would make their extended, less painful lives worth living?"

"I have had time to consider only a few of the possibilities," he replied. "Their situation would be similar to that of the Hudlar amputees we will be sending home in a few weeks' time. They will have limited mobility on prosthetics, one or two of their forelimbs will remain fully functioning, and they should remain mentally and physically effective until shortly before termination. I shall have to discuss the physiological details with Thornnastor before I can be certain of this, but—"

"It is a fair assumption, Conway," the Tralthan broke in. "I have no doubt that you are right."

"Thank you, sir," Conway said, feeling his face growing warm at the compliment. To O'Mara he went on, "On Hudlar medical science is in the early stages and for some time it will be primarily concerned with the treatment of diseases in the very young, since the adult members of the species do not take sick. These pediatric cases, although ill, remain very active and require only minimal restraint and supervision while the administered medication is doing its work. Our aged amputees will still be physically capable of withstanding without injury the enthusiasm and playfulness of the half-ton Hudlar toddlers, and we are already training the first of a line of FROB pediatric nurses who will be able to instruct them..."

Mention of that very personable female-mode nurse had excited his Hudlar mind-partner, so Conway had to spend a few seconds telling it to behave itself. But when he tried to return his mind to what he had been about to say, memories of his extremely aged but alert great-grandmother and, at the time, only friend welled up in his mind. That touched off a sudden, intensely strong feeling of sorrow from Khone over the loss of parental physical contact, which was so necessary for the maintenance of mental coherency in Gogleskan society, and which occurred at a very early age. He felt with Khone the past loss of that love and warmth and the expectation of future loss when its offspring would be born and remain close all too briefly before it departed. And strangely, although Khone's presence had been reacting against nearly all of the material being thrown up by Conway and his other mind-partners, the little Gogleskan was able to consider the sight and sounds and memories of Conway's incredibly old and fragile first friend without the slightest hint of distress.

This was important, he knew, because there were indications that the Gogleskan's mind was not entirely repelled by the thought of the geriatric FROBs, either. A bridge was being built between Khone and the other species, and Conway began blinking rapidly because his tear ducts seemed suddenly to have developed a leak.

He felt Murchison's hand squeezing his arm as she said urgently, "What's wrong?"

"Conway," O'Mara said, sounding concerned, "are you still with us?"

"Sorry, my mind went off at a tangent," he said, clearing his throat. "I'm all right. In fact, I feel very well indeed."

"I see," O'Mara said. "But I would like to discuss the reasons for and the content of your tangential thinking at a more convenient time. Continue."

"In common with elderly members of the majority of the intelligent species," Conway resumed, "the very old Hudlars have a close affinity with the very young, and a great deal of benefit can be derived from this relationship by both parties if they are placed together. The aged entities are at the stage loosely described as second childhood, when the memories and feelings of their own younger days are thrown into prominence, and they have nothing much to do with their remaining time. The children would have an adult playmate who understands them, who enjoys their company, and who is not, like the younger adults and parents, perhaps too deeply concerned with the day-to-day business of life to have enough time to spend with them.

"Provided the geriatric amputee idea is acceptable to them," he continued, "I think they would be prime candidates for pediatric nursing training. The less elderly, whose mental age would be significantly greater, could be trained as teachers of older children and preadolescents. They might also be usefully engaged in supervising automated production processes, or on watch-keeping duty on the weather control stations, or as—"

"Enough!" O'Mara said, holding up one hand. He went on caustically. "Leave me something to do, Conway, to justify my existence. At least, your uncharacteristic behavior of a few minutes ago is no longer a mystery. The childhood material in your psych file and your suggestion regarding the geriatric Hudlars fully explain your temporary loss of control.

"Regarding your original question," O'Mara went on, "I cannot give you a quick answer, but I shall call up my Hudlar material at once and start work on it. You've given me too much to think about for me to be able to go back to sleep now."

"I'm sorry," Conway said, but the Chief Psychologist's face had already gone from the screen.

"And I'm sorry for the delay as well," he said to Thornnastor. "But now at last we can talk about the Protector..."

He broke off as the blue "Vacate" light began flashing on their table, indicating that they had remained for longer than was necessary to consume the food which had been ordered, and that they should move away so as to release the table for other would-be diners, of which there was a large number waiting.

"Your office or mine?" Thornnastor said.

Chapter 19

FIRST contact with the species known as the Protectors of the Unborn had been made by *Rhabwar* when the ambulance ship had answered a distress signal from a vessel which had been transporting two members of that species under restraint. It discovered that the Protectors had broken free, and while they had been killing the ship's crew, one of them had died as well.

The surviving Protector had delivered itself of its Unborn shortly before it, too, died. That newly born Protector was the patient who, after more than a year's sojourn in Sector General, was about to give birth in its turn. The body of its parent had been thoroughly investigated by Pathology and had furnished information which might enable them to deliver the Unborn without it suffering complete obliteration of the higher functions of its mind.

"... The primary purpose of the forthcoming operation is to save the mind of the Unborn," he repeated, looking around the crowded observation gallery before he returned his attention to the ward below, where the furiously battling Protector was engaging its life-support system and two Hudlar attendants in total war. "The problems are physical, surgical, and endocrinological, and Diagnostician Thornnastor and I have discussed little else for the past two days. And now, for the benefit of the support and after-care team members who have just joined us, as well as for the observers and the others who will be studying the recordings later, I shall briefly summarize the available information on this case.

"The adult, nonintelligent Protector is physiological classification FSOJ," Conway went on. "As you can see, it is a large, immensely strong being with a heavy, slitted carapace from which protrude four thick tentacles, a heavy, serrated tail, and a head. The tentacles terminate in a cluster of sharp, bony projections so that they resemble spiked clubs. The main features of the head are the well-protected, recessed eyes, the upper and lower mandibles, and teeth which are capable of deforming all but the strongest metal alloys.

"Flip it over, please," Conway said to the two Hudlars working on the patient with thin steel bars. "And hit it harder! You won't hurt it and will, in fact, maintain it in optimum condition prior to the birth." To the observers he went on. "The four stubby legs also have osseous projections which enable these limbs to be used as weapons as well. While the underside is not armored, as is the carapace, this area is rarely open to attack, and is covered by a thick tegument which apparently gives sufficient protection. In the center of the area you can see a thin, longitudinal fissure which opens into the birth canal. It will not open, however, until a few minutes before the event.

"But first, the evolutionary and environmental background..."

The Protectors had evolved on a world of shallow, steaming sea and swampy jungles where the line of demarcation between animal and vegetable life, so far as physical mobility and aggression were concerned, was difficult to define. To survive there at all, a life-form had to fight hard and move fast, and the dominant species on that hellish world had earned its place by fighting and moving and reproducing their kind with a greater potential for survival than any of the others.

At an early stage in their evolution the utter savagery of their environment had forced them into a physiological configuration which gave maximum protection to the vital organs. The brain, heart, lungs, and womb were all sited deep within that fantastically well-muscled and protected body, and compressed into a relatively small volume. During gestation the organ displacement was considerable, because the fetus had to grow virtually to maturity before birth. It was rarely that they were able to survive the reproduction of more than three of their kind, because an aging parent was usually too weak to defend itself against the attack of a hungry last-born.

But the principal reason why the Protectors of the Unborn had risen to dominance on their world was that their young were already educated in the techniques of survival *before they were born.*

The process had begun simply as the transmission of a complex set of survival instincts at the genetic level, but the close juxtaposition of the brains of the parent and the developing embryo led to an effect analogous to induction of the electrochemical activity associated with thought.

The fetuses became short-range telepaths receiving everything the parents saw or felt or in any other way experienced.

And even before the growth of the fetus was complete, there was another embryo beginning to take form inside the first one, and the new one was also increasingly aware of the world outside its self-fertilizing grandparent. Gradually the telepathic range had increased so that communication became possible between embryos whose parents were close enough to see each other.

To minimize damage to the parent's internal organs, the growing fetus was paralyzed while in the womb, with no degradation of later muscle function. But the prebirth deparalyzing process, or possibly the birth itself, also caused a complete loss of sentience and telepathic ability. A newborn Protector, it seemed, would not last very long in its incredibly savage environment if the purity of its survival instincts was clouded by the ability to think.

"... With nothing to do but receive information from their outside world," Conway went on, "and exchange thoughts with other Unborn, and try to widen their telepathic range by tuning to nonsentient life-forms around them, the embryos developed minds of great power and intelligence. But they cannot build anything, or engage in any cooperative physical activity, or keep written records, or, indeed, do anything at all to influence their parents and Protectors who have to fight and kill and eat continuously to maintain their unsleeping bodies and the Unborn within them."

There was a moment's silence which was broken only by the muffled clanking and thumping sounds made by the mechanical life-support system and the Hudlars, who together were laboring hard to make the FSOJ parent-to-be feel right at home. Then the Lieutenant in charge of the technical support team spoke up.

"I have asked this question already," he said quietly, "but I have trouble accepting the answer. Is it really true that we must continue beating the patient even while the birth is taking place?"

"Correct, Lieutenant," Conway said. "Before, during, and after. The only advance warning we will have of the event will be a marked increase in the Protector's activity level approximately half an hour before the birth. On its home world this activity would be aimed at clearing the immediate area of predators so as to give the young one an increased chance of survival.

"It will come out fighting," Conway added, "and its

life-support must be the same as that needed by its parent except that the violence we administer will be scaled down, very slightly, because of its smaller size."

There were several beings in the gallery making untranslatable sounds of incredulity. Thornnastor gave a peremptory rumble and added its considerable weight, both physical and intellectual, to Conway's previous remarks.

"You must all realize and accept without question," the Diagnostician said ponderously, "that continual violence is normal for this creature. The FSOJ must remain in a condition of stress in order that its quite complex endocrine system will function properly. It requires, and has evolved the ability to accept, the continuous release of a hormone into its system which is the equivalent of Kelgian thullis or Earth-human adrenaline.

"Should the release of this hormone be inhibited," the Tralthan went on, "by the withdrawal of the ever-present threat of imminent injury or death, the Protector's movements become sluggish and erratic, and if the attack is not quickly resumed, unconsciousness follows. If the period of unconsciousness is prolonged, irreversible changes take place in the endocrine systems of both Protector and Unborn leading to termination."

This time the words were followed by an attentive silence. Conway indicated the ward below and said, "We shall now take you as close to the patient as it is possible to go in safety. You observers will be shown the details of the Protector's life-support mechanisms, and of the smaller version in the side-ward which will accommodate the young one when it arrives, both of which resemble nothing so much as the instruments of interrogation used during a very unsavory period in Earth's history. You new team-members will familiarize yourselves with these mechanisms and with the work expected of you, and ask as many questions as necessary to ensure that you fully understand your duties. But above all, do not be kind or gentle with this patient. That will not help it at all."

The various feet, tentacles, and pincers were beginning

to shuffle, slither, and scrape along the floor as they turned toward the gallery exit. Conway held up his hand.

"Let me remind you once again," he said very seriously. "The purpose of this operation is not simply to assist at the FSOJ's birth, which will take place with or without our assistance, believe me. It is to ensure that the Unborn and soon-to-be new Protector retains the same level of intelligence and the telepathic ability it now possesses within the womb."

Thornnastor made a quiet sound which to the Tralthan component of Conway's mind signified pessimism and anxiety. Following two days of consultations with the Diagnostician, the precise details of the forthcoming operative procedure had still to be finalized. Radiating a confidence which he did not feel, he discussed the functioning of the combination operating frame and gimbal-mounted cage which accommodated the Protector before taking them through to the side-ward designed to receive its offspring.

Nicknamed the Rumpus Room by the maintenance engineers responsible for its construction, the ward was more than half-filled by a hollow, cylindrical structure, wide enough to allow unrestricted passage of the FSOJ infant, which curved and twisted back on itself so that the occupant would be able to use all of the available floor area of the ward in which to exercise. The entry point into this continuous cylinder was a heavily reinforced door in the side-wall, which was otherwise composed of an immensely strong open latticework of metal. The cylinder floor was shaped to reproduce the uneven ground and natural obstacles, such as the mobile and voracious trip-roots found on the Protector's home planet, and the open sections gave the occupant a continuous view of the screens positioned around the outer surface of the cylinder. Onto these screens were projected moving tri-di pictures of indigenous plant and animal life which the occupant would normally encounter.

The open structure also enabled the medical team to bring to bear on their patient the more positive aspects of life-support system—the fearsome-looking mechanisms positioned between the projection screens which were designed to beat, tear, and jab at the occupant with any desired degree of frequency or force.

Everything possible had been done to make the new arrival feel at home.

"As you are already aware," Conway went on, "the Unborn, by virtue of its telepathic faculty, is constantly aware of the events taking place outside its parent. We are not telepaths and may not be capable of receiving its thoughts, even during the period of intense mental stress which occurs just prior to birth, when it is transmitting at maximum power because it knows that its mind and personality are about to be obliterated.

"There are several telepathic races known to the Federation," he continued, his mind returning to its one and only contact with a telepathic Unborn. "These are usually species who have evolved this faculty so that their common organic receiver/transmitters are automatically in tune. For this reason telepathic contact between the members of different telepathic races is not always possible. When mental contact occurs between one of these entities and a nontelepath, it usually means that the faculty in the nontelepath is either dormant or atrophied. When such contact occurs the experience can be highly uncomfortable, but there are no physical changes in the brain affected, nor is there any lasting psychological damage."

As he switched on the Rumpus Room's screens and began projecting the visual record of that first, incredibly violent birth, his mind was adding the extra-sensory dimension of his own, minutes-long telepathic contact with the Unborn so soon to be born.

Conway was aware that his fists were clenched, and that beside him Murchison's face was pale as she watched the screen. Once again the rampaging Protector tried to get at them by battering at the partly open inner seal of the air lock. The opening was five or six inches wide, just enough for the pathologist, *Rhabwar*'s injured Captain, and Conway to see and hear and record everything which was happening. But their position was not a secure one.

The Protector's hard-tipped tentacles had already wreaked havoc in the lock antechamber, tearing out sections of metal plating and deforming the underlying structure, and the lock's inner seal was not all that thick.

Their only safety lay in the fact that the lock antechamber was weightless, and the flailing tentacles of the Protector sent it spinning helplessly away from every wall or obstruction they encountered, which simply increased its anger and the savagery of its attack. It also made it more difficult to observe the birth which was taking place. But the violence of the Protector's attack was beginning to diminish. Weightlessness combined with physical damage sustained during encounters with the ship's now-dead crew and the subsequent malfunctioning of the on-board life-support system had left it with barely enough strength to complete the birth process, which was already well advanced as the parent spun slowly to give a good if intermittent view of the emergence of the Unborn.

Conway's mind was on an aspect of the birth which the recording could not reproduce—the last few moments of telepathic contact with the fetus before it left its parent and became just another vicious, insensate, completely nonsentient young Protector—and for a moment he could not speak.

Thornnastor must have sensed his difficulty because it reached past him and froze the picture. In its ponderous, lecturing manner it said, "You can see that the head and most of the carapace have appeared, and that the limbs which project from it are limp and unmoving. The reason for this is that the secretions which are released to reverse the prebirth paralysis of the Unborn, and at the same time obliterate all cerebral activity not associated with survival, have not yet taken effect. Up to this point the expulsion of the Unborn is solely the responsibility of the parent Protector."

In the characteristically forthright manner of a Kelgian, one of the nurses asked, "Is the nonsentient parent to be considered expendable?"

Thornnastor curled an eye to regard Conway, whose

mind was still fixed immovably on the circumstances of that earlier birth.

"That is not our intention," the Tralthan said when he did not respond. "The parent Protector was once a sentient Unborn, and is capable of producing anything up to three more sentient Unborn. Should the circumstances arise where a decision is needed whether to assist the birth of the sentient infant at the expense of the life of the presently nonsentient parent, or to allow the birth to proceed normally so that we end with two nonsentient Protectors, that must be the decision of the Surgeon-in-Charge.

"If the latter decision was to be considered," it went on, with one eye still fixed on Conway, "it could be argued in support that with two Protectors, a young and an old one who will both produce telepathic embryos in time, we will have another chance or chances to solve the problem. But this would mean subjecting the two FSOJs to lengthy gestation periods in a highly artificial life-support system, which might have long-term ill effects on the new embryos, and would simply mean deferring the decision. The whole procedure would have to be repeated with, in all likelihood, the same decision having to be taken by a different Surgeon-in-Charge."

Murchison's eyes were on him as well, and she was looking worried. Those last few words had been something more than a not particularly direct answer to the nurse's question; they were in the nature of a professional warning. Conway was being reminded that he was still very much on probation, and that the Diagnostician-in-Charge of Pathology did not, in spite of its seniority, bear the ultimate responsibility for this case. But still he could not speak.

"You will observe that the Unborn's tentacles are beginning to move, but slowly," Thornnastor continued. "And now it is beginning to pull itself out of the birth canal . . ."

It had been at that moment that the soundless telepathic voice in Conway's mind had lost its clarity. There had been a feeling of pain and confusion and deep anxiety muddying up the clear stream of communication, but the final message from the Unborn had been a simple one.

To be born is to die, friends, the silent voice had said. *My mind and my telepathic faculty are being destroyed, and I am becoming a Protector with my own Unborn to protect while it grows and thinks and tries to make contact with you.*

Please cherish it.

The trouble with telepathic communication, Conway thought bitterly, was that it lacked the ambiguity and verbal misdirection and diplomatic lying which was possible with the spoken word. A telepathic promise had no loopholes. It was impossible to break one without a serious loss of self-respect.

And now the Unborn with whom he had experienced mind-to-mind contact was his patient, a Protector with the Unborn he had promised to cherish about to enter the highly complex and alien world of Sector General. He was still not sure how best to proceed—or, more accurately, which of several unsatisfactory options to adopt.

To nobody in particular he said suddenly, "We don't even know that the fetus has grown normally in hospital conditions. Our reproduction of the environment may not have been accurate enough. The Unborn may not have developed sentience, much less the telepathic faculty. There have been no indications of..."

He broke off as a series of musical trills and clicks came from the ceiling above their heads, and from their translators came the words, "You may not be entirely correct in your assumption, friend Conway."

"Prilicla!" Murchison said, and added unnecessarily, "You're back!"

"Are you...well?" Conway asked. He was thinking of the Menelden casualties and the hell it must have been for an empath to be placed in charge of classifying them.

"I am well, friend Conway," Prilicla replied, the legs holding it to the ceiling twitching slowly as it bathed in the emotional radiation of friendship and concern emanating from those below. "I was careful to direct operations from as great a distance as possible, just as I am remaining well clear of your patient in the outer ward. The Protector's emotional radiation is unpleasant to me, but not so the radiation from the Unborn.

"Mentation of a high order is present," the Cinrusskin went on. "Regrettably, I am an empath rather than a true telepath, but the feelings I detect are of frustration which is caused, I would guess, by its inability to communicate with those outside, together with feelings of confusion and awe which are predominating."

"Awe?" Conway said, then added, "If it has been trying to communicate, we've felt nothing, not even the faintest tickle."

Prilicla dropped from the ceiling, executed a neat loop, and fluttered to the top of a nearby instrument cabinet so that the DBLFs and DBDGs present would not have to strain their cervical vertabrae watching it. "I cannot be completely sure, friend Conway, because feelings are less trustworthy for the conveyance of intelligence than coherent thoughts, but it seems to me that the trouble may simply be one of mental overcrowding. During your original contact with the then Unborn and present Protector, the being had only three minds to consider, those of friends Murchison, Fletcher, and yourself. The other crew and medical team members were aboard *Rhabwar* and at extreme telepathic range.

"Here there may be too many minds," the empath went on, "minds of a bewildering variety and degree of complexity, including two"—its eyes turned to regard Thornnastor and Conway—"which seem to contain a multiplicity of entities, and which might be truly confusing, and awe-inspiring."

"You're right, of course," Conway said. He thought for a moment, then went on. "I was hoping for telepathic contact with the Unborn before and during the birth. In this case the assistance of a conscious and cooperating patient would be of great help indeed. But you can see the size of the operating room staff and technical support people. There are dozens of them. I can't simply send them all away."

Prilicla began to tremble again, this time in agitation

over the additional worry it was causing Conway, when its intention had been only to reassure him regarding the mental health of the Unborn. It made another attempt to improve the quality of its friend's emotional radiation.

"I called in at the Hudlar ward as soon as I got back," the Cinrusskin said, "and I must say that your people did very well. Those were bad cases I sent in, as nearly hopeless as it is possible to be, friend Conway, but you lost only one of them. It was very fine work, even though friend O'Mara says that you have handed him another freshly boiled vegetable."

"I think," Murchison said, laughing as she translated the translated words, "it means another hot potato."

"O'Mara?" Conway asked.

"The Chief Psychologist was talking to one of your patients," Prilicla replied, "and assessing its nonmedical condition after visiting one of the Hudlars in the geriatric section. Friend O'Mara knew that I was coming to see you, and it said to tell you that a signal from Goglesk has arrived to the effect that your friend Khone wants to come to the hospital as soon as—"

"Khone is sick, badly injured?" Conway broke in, the persona of his Gogleskan mind-partner and his feelings for the little being pushing everything and everybody else out of his mind. He knew, because Khone had known, of the many diseases and accidents to which the FOKTs were prey, and for which very little could be done because to approach each other for help was to invite disaster. Whatever had happened to Khone, it must have been pretty bad for it to want to come to Sector General, where the worst nightmares of its mind were a physical actuality.

"No, no, friend Conway," Prilicla said, trembling again with the violence of his emotional radiation. "Khone's condition is neither serious nor urgent. But it has asked that you, personally, collect it and convey it to the hospital lest fear of your physically monstrous friends causes it to change its mind. Friend O'Mara's precise words were that you seem to be attracting some odd maternity cases these days."

"But it can't be volunteering to come *here*!" Conway

protested. He knew that Khone was mature and capable of producing offspring. There was nothing in the Gogleskan's mind regarding recent sexual encounters, which meant that it must have happened since Conway had left Goglesk. He began doing calculations based on the FOKT gestation period.

"That was my reaction as well, friend Conway," Prilicla said. "But friend O'Mara pointed out that you had lived with and adapted to the presence of your Gogleskan friend and that it, Heaven help it, had been similarly influenced by your Earth-human mind. That was the second boiled vegetable; the other was the geriatric Hudlar business.

"Sorting out the psychoses of a FOKT parent-to-be and offspring scared of their prehistoric shadows was not going to be easy," the empath went on, "and the geriatric Hudlar problem had grown to the stage where it was taking up practically all of his time. It sounded very irritated and at times angry, did friend O'Mara, but its emotional radiation was at variance with the spoken words. There were strong feelings of anticipation and excitement, as if it was looking forward to the challenge..."

It broke off and began trembling again. Beside the instrument cabinet it was clinging to, Thornnastor was lifting and lowering its six elephantine feet one at a time and in no particular sequence. Murchison looked at the Diagnostician, and even though she was not an empath, she knew her chief well enough to be able to recognize a very impatient Tralthan.

"This is all very interesting, Prilicla," she said gently, "but unlike that of Khone, the condition of the patient awaiting our attention in the outer ward is both serious and urgent."

Chapter 20

IN spite of everyone else's sense of urgency the Protector seemed to be in no particular hurry to deliver its Unborn. Conway was secretly relieved. It gave him more time to think, to consider alternative procedures and, if he was honest with himself, more time to dither.

The normally phlegmatic Thornnastor, with three eyes on the patient and one on the scanner projection, was slowly stamping one foot as it watched the lack of activity in the area of the Protector's womb. Murchison was dividing her attention between the screen and the Kelgian nurse who was in charge of the patient's restraints, and Prilicla was a distant, fuzzy blob clinging to the ceiling at the other end of the ward, where the emotional radiation from the Protector was bearable if not comfortable, and linked to the OR Team by communicator.

It was there purely out of clinical curiosity, the little empath had insisted. But the true reason was probably that it sensed Conway's anxiety regarding the coming operation and it wanted to help.

"Of the alternative procedures you have mentioned," Thornnastor said suddenly, "the first is slightly more desirable. But prematurely enlarging the birth opening and withdrawing the Unborn while at the same time clamping off those gland ducts . . . It's tricky, Conway. You could be faced with an awakened and fully active young Protector tearing and eating its way out of the parent. Or have you now decided that the parent is expendable?"

Conway's mind was filled again with the memory of his telepathic contact with an Unborn, an Unborn who had been born as a mindless Protector, *this* Protector. He knew that he was not being logical, but he did not want to discard a being whose mind he had known so intimately simply because, for evolutionary reasons, it had suffered a form of brain death.

"No," Conway said firmly.

"The other alternatives are even worse," the Tralthan said.

"I was hoping you'd feel that way," Conway said.

"I understand," Thornnastor said. "But neither am I greatly in favor of your primary suggestion. The procedure is radical, to say the least, and unheard-of when the species concerned possesses a carapace. Such delicate work on a fully conscious and mobile patient is—"

"The patient," Conway broke in, "will be conscious, and immobilized."

"It seems, Conway," it said, speaking quietly for a Tralthan, "that there is some confusion in your mind due, perhaps, to the multiplicity of tapes occupying it. Let me remind you that the patient cannot be immobilized for any lengthy period of time, either by physical restraint or anesthetics, without irreversible metabolic changes taking place which lead quickly to unconsciousness and termination. The FSOJ is constantly moving and constantly under attack, and the response of its endocrine system is such that... But you know this as well as I do, Conway! Are you well? Is there psychological, perhaps temporary, distress? Would you like me to assume charge for a time?"

Murchison had been listening to her communicator and had missed Thornnastor's earlier words. She looked worriedly at Conway, obviously wondering what was wrong with him, or what her Chief thought was wrong with him; then she said, "Prilicla called me. It didn't want to interrupt you during what might have been an important clinical discussion between its superiors, but it reports a steady increase and change in the quality of emotional radiation emanating from both the Protector and its Unborn. The indications are that the Protector is preparing itself for a major effort, and this in turn has caused an increase in the level of mentation in the Unborn. Prilicla wants to know if you have detected any signs of an attempt at telepathic contact. It says the Unborn is trying very hard."

Conway shook his head. To Thornnastor he said, "With respect, this information was contained in my original report on the FSOJ life-form to you, and my memory is unimpaired. I thank you for the offer to take charge, and I welcome your advice and assistance, but I am not psychologically distressed, and my mental confusion is at a similar level to that at which I normally operate."

"Your remarks about immobilizing the patient suggested otherwise," Thornnastor said after a short pause. "I'm glad that you feel well, but I am not completely reassured regarding your surgical intentions."

"And I'm not completely sure that I'm right," Conway replied. "But my indecision has gone, and my intended procedure is based on the assumption that we have been too heavily influenced by the FSOJ's life-support machinery and the insistence on physical mobility . . ."

Out of the corner of his eye he saw the figure of Prilicla grow more blurred as it began to tremble violently. He broke off and said into his communicator, "Withdraw, little friend. Keep in contact but move out into the corridor. The emotional radiation around here is going to be pretty savage stuff, so move back quickly."

"I was about to do so, friend Conway," it replied. "But the quality of your own emotional radiation is not pleasant for either of us. There is determination, anxiety, and the feeling that you are forcing yourself to do something which normally you would not do. My apologies. In my concern for a friend I am discussing material which should properly be considered privileged. I am leaving now. Good luck, friend Conway."

Before he could reply one of the Kelgians, its fur rippling with urgency, reported that the birth opening was beginning to enlarge.

"Relax," he said, studying the scanner picture. "Nothing is happening internally as yet. Please position the patient on its left side with a right upper dorsal presentation. The operative field will be centered fifteen inches to the right of the carapacial median line in the position marked.

Continue with the present life-support arrangements, but with a bit more enthusiasm if you can manage it, until I tell you to stop. On my signal the restraints team will immobilize the patient's limbs, being particularly careful to stretch the tentacles to full lateral extension and to anchor them with clamps and pressor beams. I have just decided that this job will be difficult enough without the patient jerking and wriggling all over the table while we are operating. While the operation is in progress, I want the minimum number of OR and support staff present, and those who are present must discipline their thinking as I will direct. Do you understand your instructions?"

"Yes, Doctor," the Kelgian replied, but its fur was showing doubt and disapproval. A series of shocks transmitted through his shoes from the floor told him that Thornnastor was stamping its feet again.

"Sorry about the interruptions," he said to the Tralthan. "I had been about to suggest that complete immobilization might be possible during the period necessary to complete the operation without serious damage to the patient. To follow my reasoning in this we must first consider what happens before, during, and after a major operation on any of the life-forms who, unlike the FSOJ, become periodically and frequently unconscious in the condition we know as sleep. In such cases—"

"They are tranquilized to minimize preoperative worry," Thornnastor broke in, its feet still displaying its impatience, "anesthetized during the procedure, and monitored postoperatively until the metabolism and vital signs have stabilized. This is elementary, Conway."

"I realize that," he replied, "and I'm hoping that the solution to the problem is also elementary."

He paused for a moment to marshal his thoughts, then went on. "You will agree that a normal patient, even though it is deeply anesthetized, reacts against the surgical intervention which is taking place. If it was conscious it would want to do what the Protector is trying to do to our operating staff, that is, trying to kill them and/or escape from the threat they represent. Even when anesthetized the normal patient is reacting unconsciously to a condition of severe stress, its system has been flooded with its equivalent of adrenaline, the available supplies of blood, sugars, and oxygen have been stepped up, and it is ready to fight or flee. This is a condition which our Protector enjoys, if that is the correct word, permanently. It is constantly fighting and fleeing because it is constantly under attack."

Thornnastor and Murchison were watching him intently, but neither spoke.

"Because we are showing it pictures in three dimensions and in quite terrifying detail of its natural environment," Conway went on, "and we will be attacking it, surgically, with an intensity that it has certainly not experienced before, I am hoping to fool it and its endocrine system into believing that its limbs are still engaged in fighting off the attack or trying to flee from it. The limbs are, after all, fighting against the restraints, and the muscular effort needed is comparable.

"We will be attacking it," he concluded, "with a major cesarean procedure through the carapace rather than in the abdominal area, without benefit of anesthesia, and I expect that there will be enough pain and confusion in its mind to make it forget that its body is not in motion, at least for the relatively short time it will take to complete the operation."

Murchison was staring at him, her face expressionless but as pale as her white uniform. The full meaning of what he had just been saying dawned on Conway, and he felt sick and ashamed. The words were in direct contradiction to everything he had been taught as a healer and a bringer of comfort. *You must be cruel to be kind*, someone had told him once, but surely they had not meant this cruel.

"The Earth-human DBDG component of my mind," Thornnastor said slowly, "is feeling shock and disgust at such unheard-of behavior."

"This DBDG," Conway said, tapping himself angrily on the chest, "feels the same way. But your taped DBDG never had to deliver a Protector."

"Neither," Thornnastor said, "has anyone else."

Murchison was about to speak when there was a double interruption.

"The birth opening is beginning to widen," the Kelgian charge nurse reported, "and there is a small change in the position of the fetus."

"The emotional radiation from both entities is reaching a peak," Prilicla said on the communicator. "You will not have long to wait, friend Conway. Please do not distress yourself. Your clinical thinking is usually trustworthy."

The Cinrusskin invariably said the right thing, Conway thought gratefully as Thornnastor followed him to the operating frame.

They checked the underside first, moving as close as they could while still avoiding the Protector's wildly thrashing legs and the Hudlar who was jabbing at them with a metal bar to reproduce the attacks of the small, sharp-toothed predators of its home world. The musculature associated with the limbs was in constant, writhing motion, and in the medial area the birth opening was slowly lengthening and widening.

For the recorders, Conway said, "Junior will not be coming out this way. Normally, a cesarean procedure calls for a long, abdominal incision through which the fetus is removed. That course is contraindicated in this case for two reasons. It would involve cutting through several of the leg muscles, and because this being is incapable of resting a damaged limb while healing takes place, the clinical injury would never heal and the limbs concerned would be permanently affected. Secondly, we would be going in very close to the two glands which, we are virtually certain, contain the secretions which reverse the prebirth paralysis and obliterate the mind. Both, as you can see in the scanner, are connected to the umbilical and are compressed, and their contents discharged into the fetus, during the later stages of the birth process. In this physiological classification, a traditional cesarean entry would almost certainly compress these glands prematurely, and the purpose of the operation, the delivery of an intelligent Unborn, would be defeated. So we'll have to do it the hard way, by going through the carapace at an angle which will cause minimum disturbance to the underlying vital organs."

While the charge nurse had been positioning the Protector for the operation, the movements of the Unborn had been imperceptible, but now the scanner showed a slow, steady motion toward the birth canal. He forced himself to walk around to the other side of the operating frame, when his instinct was to break into an undignified gallop; then he checked that Thornnastor and Murchison were in position and said quietly, "Immobilize the patient."

The four dorsal tentacles were at full extension, motionless except for the barest tremor caused by their efforts to overcome the restraints. He tried not to think of the devastation even one of those limbs would cause among the OR staff if it succeeded in pulling free, or that he was closest and would be the first casualty.

"It is desirable—in fact it may be vitally necessary—that we establish telepathic contact with the Unborn before the operation is completed," Conway said above the buzzing of his surgical saw. "The first time such contact took place, there was only one physiological classification present, the Earth-human DBDGs Pathologist Murchison, Captain Fletcher of *Rhabwar*, and I. A multiplicity of physiological types and thought patterns may be making it difficult to make contact, or it may be that DBDGs are fractionally easier to communicate with telepathically. For this reason..."

"Do you wish me to leave?" Thornnastor asked.

"No," Conway said very firmly. "I need your assistance, as both a surgeon and an endocrinologist. But it would be helpful if you tried to bring forward the DBDG component of your mind and concentrated on its thought processes."

"I understand," the Tralthan said.

Working quickly, Thornnastor and Conway excised a large, triangular section of carapace, then paused to control some minor bleeding from the underlying vessels. Murchison was not assisting directly, but was concentrating all of her attention on the scanner so that she could warn them if the trauma of the operation was giving indications of triggering premature delivery. They went deeper, cutting through the thick, almost transparent membrane which enclosed the lungs, clamping it back.

"Prilicla?" Conway asked.

"The patient is feeling anger, fear, and pain in steadily increasing intensity. It does not seem to be aware of anything other than that it is being savagely attacked and is defending itself. Apparently it has not realized that it isn't moving, and there are no emotional indications of endocrine misfunction...

"The effect of this attack on the Unborn," the empath went on, "is of markedly heightened sensation and mentation levels. There is greater awareness and intense effort. It is trying very hard to contact you, friend Conway."

"It's mutual," he replied. But he knew that too much of his mind was being devoted to the surgical aspect just then and not enough to communication for there to be any hope of success.

In the FSOJ the heart was not situated between the lungs, but there were several major blood vessels traversing the area, and these with their associated digestive organs had to be moved out of the way without cutting—surgery had to be kept to the irreducible minimum when the patient would be mobile minutes after the operation was completed. As he pressed them carefully apart and locked the dilators in position, he knew that the circulation in several of those vessels was being seriously impaired, and that he was constricting one of the lungs and rendering it little more than sixty percent effective.

"It will be for a short time only," he said defensively in answer to Thornnastor's unspoken comment, "and the patient is on pure oxygen, which should make up the deficiency..."

He broke off as his exploring fingers moved deeper and encountered a long, flat bone which had no business being there. He looked quickly at the position of his hand in the scanner and saw that he was, in fact, touching not a bone but one of the muscles of a dorsal tentacle. The muscle had locked in spasm as the patient tried to pull the limb free of the restrains. Or perhaps it was simply reacting—as did the members of other species who locked mandibles or clenched fists—to unbearable pain.

Suddenly his hands were trembling as all of his medically trained and caring alter egos reacted to that thought.

"Friend Conway," Prilicla said, its voice distorted by more than the translator, "you are distressing me. Concentrate on what you are doing and not on what you are feeling!"

"Don't bully me, Prilicla!" he snapped. Then he laughed as he realized the ridiculous thing he had just said, and went back to work. A few minutes later he was feeling out the contours of the Unborn's upper carapace and its limp dorsal tentacles. He grasped one of them and began to pull gently.

"That entity," Thornnastor rumbled at him, "is supposed to come out of the womb fighting and able to inflict serious damage with those particular limbs. I don't think the tentacle would come off if you were to pull a little harder, Conway."

He pulled harder and the Unborn moved, but only a few inches. The young FSOJ was no lightweight, and Conway was already sweating with the effort. He slipped his other hand down into the opening and found another dorsal tentacle; then he began a two-handed pull with one knee braced against the operating frame.

He had performed more delicate feats of surgery and manipulation in his time, Conway thought sourly, but even with this unsubtle procedure the little beastie was refusing to budge.

"The passage is too tight," he said, gasping. "So tight I think suction is holding it in. Can you slide a long probe between the inner face of the dilator and the inner surface of the carapace, just there, so that we can release . . ."

"The Protector is beginning to weaken, friend Conway," Prilicla said, the mere fact that it had been impolite enough to interrupt its Seniors stressing the urgency of its report.

But Thornnastor was moving in before the empath had finished speaking, using the slim, tapering extremity of a manipulatory tentacle instead of the probe. There was a brief hissing sound as suction was released. The Tralthan's tentacle moved deeper, curled around the Unborn's rear legs, and began helping Conway to lift and slide it out. Within a few seconds it was clear, but still connected to its parent by the umbilical.

"Well," Conway said, placing the newly born Unborn on the tray Murchison had already placed to receive it, "that was the easy part. And if ever we needed a conscious and cooperative patient, now is the time."

"The Unborn's feelings are of intense frustration verging on despair, friend Conway," Prilicla reported. "It must still be trying to contact you. The Protector's emotional radiation is weakening, and there is a change in the texture which suggests that it is becoming aware of its lack of motion."

To Thornnastor, Conway said quickly, "If we reduce the dilation, which is unnecessary now that the Unborn is out, that will enable the constricted lung to operate more effectively. How much room do we need to work in there?"

Thornnastor made a noise which did not translate, then went on. "I require a fairly small opening through which to work, and I am the endocrinologist. Those ridiculous DBDG knuckles and wrists are physiologically unsuited to this particular job. With respect, I suggest that you concentrate on the Unborn."

"Right," Conway said. He appreciated the Tralthan's recognition of the fact that he was in charge even though he was, at best, only a temporary Diagnostician whose recent operative behavior would almost certainly ensure the temporary nature of his rank. Without looking up he went on. "All non-DBDG members of the OR and support teams move back to the ward entrance. Do not talk, and try to keep your minds as blank as possible by looking at and thinking about a clear area of wall or ceiling, so as to make it easier for the telepath to tune in to the three of us here. Move quickly, please."

The scanner was already showing two of the Tralthan's slim tentacles sliding down into the womb on each side of the umbilical. They came to rest above two ovoid swellings which, over the past few days, had grown to the size and coloration of large, red plums. There was adequate space inside the now-empty womb for a number of different surgical procedures to be carried out, but Thornnastor, of necessity, was doing nothing.

"The two glands are identical, Conway," the Tralthan said, "and there is no rapid method of telling which secretes the deparalyzing agent and which the mind destroyer. There is one chance in two of being right. Shall I apply gentle pressure, and to which one?"

"No, wait," Conway said urgently. "I've had second thoughts about that. If the birth had been normal, both glands would have been compressed while the Unborn was exiting and the secretions discharged through ducts directly into the umbilical. Considering the degree of swelling present and the tightly stretched appearance of the containing membranes, it is possible that even the most gentle pressure would cause a sudden rather than a gradual discharge of the secretions. My original idea of metering the discharge by applying gentle pressure and observing the effect on the patient was not a good one. As well, there is the possibility that both glands secrete the same agency and that it performs both functions."

"Highly unlikely," Thornnastor said, "the effects are so markedly different. Regrettably, the material has a complex and unstable biochemical structure which breaks down very quickly; otherwise the cadaver of your first Protector would have contained sufficient residual material for us to have synthesized it. This is the first occasion that samples have been available from a living Protector, but the analysis would be a lengthy process and the patients might not survive for long in their present condition."

"I completely agree," Prilicla said, sounding unusually vehement for a Cinrusskin. "The Protector is going into a panic reaction, it is becoming aware of its abnormal condition of immobility, and the indications are of general and rapid deterioration. You must withdraw and close up, friend Conway, and quickly."

"I know," Conway replied, then went on fiercely.

"*Think*! Think *at* the Unborn, of the situation it is in, of our problems, of what we are trying to do for it. I need telepathic contact before I can risk—"

"I feel irregular, spasmodic contractions increasing in severity," Thornnastor broke in. "The movements are probably abnormal and associated with the panic reaction, but there is the danger of them compressing the glands prematurely. And I don't think that establishing telepathic contact with the Unborn will help identify the correct gland. A newly born infant, however intelligent, does not usually possess detailed anatomical knowledge of its parent."

"The Protector," Murchison said from the other side of the operating frame, "is no longer fighting against its restraints."

"Friend Conway," Prilicla said, "the patient is losing consciousness."

"All *right*!" Conway snapped. He was trying desperately to think at the Unborn and for himself, but all his alter egos were trying desperately to think as well and were confusing him. Some of the answers they were throwing up did not apply, some were ridiculous, and one—he had no idea who originated it—was so ridiculously simple that it had to be tried.

"Clamp the umbilical as close as possible to those glands so as to guard against accidental discharge," Conway said quickly, "then sever the cord on the other side of the clamp to separate the parent and infant. I'll draw out the remainder of the umbilical, and you go into the glands with two needles. Evacuate the contents of each by suction and store the secretions in separate containers for later use. You might have to speed up the process by compressing the glands as well. I'd help you, but there isn't much room down there."

Thornnastor did not reply. It was already lifting one of the suction needles from its instrument tray while Murchison was switching on the pump to test it and attaching two small, sterile containers. Within a few minutes the suction needles had been introduced and both of the bulging glands were visibly growing smaller.

When the scanner showed them as flattened, red patches on opposite sides of the birth canal, Conway said, "That's enough. Withdraw. I'll help you close up. And if there's an unoccupied corner of your mind, please use it to think at the Unborn."

"All the corners of my mind are occupied by other people," Thornnastor said, "but I shall try."

Withdrawing was much easier than the entry had been because the Protector was unconscious, its muscles were relaxed, and there were no internal tensions trying to pull the sutures apart while they were being inserted. Thornnastor repaired the incision they had made in the womb; then together they eased the temporarily displaced organs back into position and sutured the thick membrane enclosing the lungs. All that remained was the replacement of the triangular section of carapace with the inert metal staples used on the hard and flexible hide of the FROB Hudlars.

The Hudlar operations felt as if they had happened years ago, Conway was thinking, when Thornnastor began stamping its feet in agitation.

"I am suffering intense discomfort in the cranial area," the Diagnostician said. While it was speaking, Murchison put a finger in her ear and began to waggle it frantically, as if trying to relieve a deep itch. Then Conway felt it, too, and gritted his teeth, because his hands were otherwise engaged.

The sensations were exactly the same as those he had experienced when the Protector, then an Unborn, had made telepathic contact during that earlier ship rescue. It was a combination of pain and intense irritation and a kind of discordant, unheard noise which mounted steadily in intensity. He had theorized about it after that first experience, and decided that a faculty which was either dormant or atrophied was being forced to perform. As in the case of a muscle long unused, there was soreness and stiffness and protest against the change in the old, comfortable order of things.

On that first occasion the discomfort had built up to a climax, and then . . .

I have been aware of the thoughts of the entities Thornnastor, Murchison, and Conway since a few moments before I was removed from my Protector, a clear, silent, and urgent voice said in their minds, from which the maddening mental itch was suddenly gone. *I am aware of your purpose, that of birthing a telepathic Unborn to become a young Protector without loss of faculties, and I am most grateful for your efforts no matter what the eventual outcome may be. I am also aware of the entity Conway's present intentions, and I urge you to act quickly. This will be my only chance. My mental faculties are dimming.*

"Leave the parent for the time being," he said firmly, "and set up to infuse Junior."

He did not tell them to make it fast, because both Murchison and Thornnastor had received that same telepathic message. With luck there might not be any permanent impairment of the Unborn's faculties, he thought, because the effect could be due to the newly born FSOJ being immobile like its parent. While the other two were working, he removed the surplus length of the umbilical and moved the infant's transporter cage to a more convenient position in readiness, should the procedure he planned be successful, to receive a suddenly active and dangerous young Protector. By the time he had done that, Thornnastor and Murchison had the infusion needle sited in the stub of the Unborn's umbilical and a length of fine tubing connecting it to one of the sterile containers of withdrawn gland secretion.

It might be the wrong one, Conway thought grimly as he eased open the delivery valve and watched the oily, yellowish secretion ooze slowly along the tube, but now the chances were much better than fifty-fifty.

"Prilicla," he said into the communicator, "I am in telepathic contact with the Unborn, who will, I hope, be able to tell me of any physical or psychological changes caused by this infusion which, because of its irreversible effects, will be delivered in minute doses until I know that I have the right one. But I need you, little friend, to serve as backup by reporting changes in its emotional radiation, changes of which it itself may not be aware. If the Unborn should break off contact, or lose consciousness, you could be its only hope."

"I understand, friend Conway," Prilicla said, moving along the ceiling toward them so as to decrease the range. "From here I can detect quite subtle changes in the Unborn's radiation, now that it is no longer being swamped by the Protector's emotional output."

Thornnastor had returned to suturing the parent's carapace, but with one eye on the scanner and another on Conway as he bent over the infusion equipment. He delivered the first minute dose.

I am not aware of any changes in my thinking other than an increasing difficulty . . . difficulty in maintaining contact with you, the silent voice sounded in his mind. *Neither am I conscious of any muscular activity.*

Conway tried another minute dose, then another followed, in desperation, by one which was not so minute.

No change, thought the Unborn.

There was no depth to the thinking, and the meaning was barely perceptible through a rush of telepathic noise. The precontact itching somewhere between his ears was returning.

"There is fear . . ." Prilicla began.

"I know there is fear," Conway broke in. "We're in telepathic contact, dammit!"

". . . On the unconscious as well as the conscious level, friend Conway," the Cinrusskin went on. "It is consciously afraid because of its physical weakening and loss of sensation due to its continued immobility. But at a lower level there is . . . Friend Conway, it may not be possible for a mind to regard itself other than subjectively, and perhaps a failing or occluded mind cannot subjectively perceive that failure."

"Little friend," Conway said, disconnecting the container he had been using and replacing it with the other one, "you're a genius!"

This time it was no minute dose because they were fast running out of time, for both patients. Conway straightened up to better observe the effect on the Unborn, then ducked frantically to avoid one of its tentacles which was swinging at his head.

"Grab it before it falls off the tray!" Conway shouted. "Forget the transporter. It's still partially paralyzed, so hold it by the tentacles and carry it to the Rumpus Room. I'd help you, but I want to protect this container..."

I am aware of an increasing feeling of physical well-being, the Unborn thought.

With Murchison gripping one of its tentacles and Thornnastor the other three, the Unborn was flopping up and down between them in its efforts to break free as Conway followed them to the door of the smaller scale FSOJ life-support complex. Using Tralthan tentacles, female Earth-human hands, and one of Conway's large feet, they were able to hold it still while he administered the remainder of the deparalyzing secretion, after which they pushed the patient inside and sealed the door.

The young Protector and recently Unborn began moving rapidly along the hollow cylinder, lashing out at the bars, clubs, and spikes which were beating and jabbing at it.

"How do you feel?" Conway asked and thought anxiously.

Fine. Very well indeed. This is exhilarating, came the reply. *But I am concerned about my parent.*

"So are we," Conway said, and led the way back to the operating frame where Prilicla was clinging to the ceiling directly above the Protector. The fact that the empath was at minimum range indicated both its concern for the patient's condition and the weakness of the FSOJ's emotional radiation.

"Life-support team!" Conway called to the beings who were waiting at the other end of the ward. "Get back here! Loosen the restraints on all limbs. Let it move, but not enough to endanger the operating team."

The suturing of the carapace had still to be completed, and with Thornnastor and him both working on it, that took about ten minutes. During that time there was no movement from the Protector other than the tiny quiverings caused by the blows and jabs being delivered by the life-support machinery. In deference to the patient's gravely weakened postoperative state, Conway had ordered the equipment to be operated at half-power and that positive pressure ventilation be used to force the FSOJ to breathe pure oxygen. But by the time the remaining sutures were in place and they had conducted a detailed scanner examination of their earlier internal work, there was still no physical response.

Somehow he had to awaken it, get through to its deeply unconscious brain, and there was only one channel of communication open. Pain.

"Step up life-support to full power," he said, concealing his desperation behind an air of confidence. "Is there any change, Prilicla?"

"No change," the empath said, trembling in the emotional gale which could only have been coming from Conway.

Suddenly he lost his temper.

"*Move*, dammit!" he shouted, bringing the edge of his hand down on the inside of the root of the nearest tentacle, which was still lying flaccidly at full extension. The area he struck was pink and relatively soft, because few of the Protector's natural enemies would have been able to make such a close approach and the tegument there was thin. Even so, it hurt his hand.

"Again, friend Conway," Prilicla said. "Hit it again, and harder!"

"Wh . . . What?" Conway asked.

Prilicla was quivering with excitement now. It said, "I think—no, I'm sure I caught a flicker of awareness just then. Hit it! Hit it again!"

Conway was about to do so when one of Thornnastor's tentacles curled tightly around his wrist. Ponderously, the Tralthan said, "Repeated misuse of that hand will not enhance the surgical dexterity of those ridiculous DBDG digits, Conway. Allow me."

The Diagnostician produced one of the dilators and brought it down heavily and accurately on the indicated area. It repeated the blows, varying the frequency and gradually increasing the power as Prilicla called, "Harder! *Harder*!"

Conway fought back the urge to break into hysterical laughter.

"Little friend," he said incredulously, "are you trying to be the Federation's first cruel and sadistic Cinrusskin? You certainly sound as if . . . Why are you running away?"

The empath was ducking and weaving its way between the lighting fixtures as it raced across the ceiling toward the ward entrance. Through the communicator it said, "The Protector is rapidly regaining consciousness and is feeling very angry. Its emotional radiation . . . Well, it is not a nice entity to be near when it is angry, or at any other time."

The relatively weak structure of the operating frame was demolished as the Protector came fully awake and began striking out in all directions with its tentacles, tail, and armored head. But the life-support machinery enclosing the frame had been designed to take such punishment, as well as hitting back. For a few minutes they stood watching the FSOJ in awed silence until Murchison laughed with evident relief.

"I suppose we can safely say," she said, "that parent and offspring are doing fine."

Thornnastor, who had one of his eyes directed at the Rumpus Room, said, "I wouldn't be too sure. The young one has almost stopped moving."

They ran and lumbered back to the scaled-down life-support system of the young Protector. A few minutes earlier they had left it charging around the system, happily battering at everything mechanical that moved. Now, Conway saw with a sudden shock of despair, it was stationary inside its cudgel-lined tunnel, and only two of its tentacles were wrapped around a thick, projecting club trying to tear it free of its mounting while the other two hung perfectly still. Before Conway could speak, there was a cool, clear, and undistressed thought floating silently in his mind.

Thank you, my friends. You have saved my parent, and you have succeeded in achieving the birth of the first intelligent and telepathic Protector. I have, with great difficulty, tuned in to the thoughts of several different life-forms in this great hospital, none of whom, with the exceptions of the entities Conway, Thornnastor, and Murchison, have been able to receive me. But there are two additional entities with whom I shall be able to communicate fully and without difficulty, because of your efforts. They are the next Unborn, who is already taking form in my parent, and the other, which I myself am carrying. I can foresee a future when a growing number of Unborn will continue their mental growth as telepathic Protectors, with the technical, cultural, and philosphical development which that will make possible . . .

The clear, calm, and quietly joyous stream of thought was suddenly clouded by anxiety.

. . . I am assuming that this delicate and difficult operation can be repeated?

"Delicate!" Thornnastor said, and made an untranslatable sound. "It was the crudest procedure I have ever encountered. Difficult, yes, but not delicate. On future occasions we will not have to play guessing games with the gland secretions. We will have the correct one synthesized and ready, and the element of risk will be greatly reduced.

"You will have your telepathic companions," the Tralthan ended. "That I promise you."

Telepathic promises were very hard to keep and even more difficult to break. Conway wanted to warn the Tralthan against making such promises too lightly, but somehow he knew that Thornnastor understood.

Thank you, and everyone else who was and will be concerned. But now I must break off contact, because the mental effort required to stay in tune with your minds is becoming too much for me. Thank you again.

"Wait," Conway said urgently. "Why have you stopped moving?"

I am experimenting. I had assumed that I would have no voluntary control over my bodily movements, but apparently this is not so. For the past few minutes, and with much mental effort, I have been able to direct all of the energy necessary to my well-being into trying to destroy this one piece of metal rather than striking out at everything. But it is extremely difficult, and I must soon relax and allow my involuntary system to resume control. That is why I am so optimistic regarding future progress for our species. With constant practice I may be able to avoid attacking, for perhaps a whole hour at a time, those around me. The fear of attack is more difficult to reproduce, and I may need advice . . .

"This is great! . . ." Conway began enthusiastically, but for a moment the thinking resumed.

. . . But I do not wish to be released from this mechanism, and risk running amok among your patients and staff. My physical self-control is far from perfect, and I realize that I am not yet ready to mix with you socially.

There was an instant of itching between his ears, then a great, mental silence, which was slowly filled by Conway's own and strangely lonely thoughts.

Chapter 21

HIS second meeting of Diagnosticians was different in that Conway thought he knew what to expect—a searching and mercilessly professional interrogation regarding his recent surgical behavior. But this time there were two non-Diagnosticians present, the Chief Psychologist and Colonel Skempton, the Monitor Corps officer in charge of the hospital's supply and maintenance. It was these two who seemed to be the center of attention, interrogation, and criticism, to such an extent that Conway felt sorry for them as well as grateful for the extra time they were giving him to prepare his defense.

Diagnostician Semlic required reassurance regarding

the power source for a new synthesizer which was being set up two levels above its dark and incredibly cold domain, particularly about the adequacy of the existing shielding against the increased risk of heat and radiation contamination of its wards. Diagnosticians Suggrod and Kursedth both wanted to know what, if any, progress had been made about providing additional accommodation for the Kelgian medical staff. Some of them were occupying the former Illensan accommodation, which, in spite of everything that had been done, still stank of chlorine.

While Colonel Skempton was trying to convince the two Kelgians that the smell was purely psychosomatic, because it did not register on his department's most sensitive detectors, Ergandhir, the Melfan Diagnostician, was already beginning to list a number of admittedly minor faults in ELNT ward equipment which were causing growing annoyance to both patients and staff. The Colonel replied that the replacement parts had been ordered, but because of their highly specialized nature, delays were to be expected. While they were still talking, Vosan, the water-breathing AMSL, began to question O'Mara regarding the desirability of assigning the diminutive and birdlike Nallajim to a ward designed for the thirty meters long, armored and tentacled Chalders, who were likely to inadvertently ingest them.

Before the Chief Psychologist could reply, the polite, sibiliant voice of the PVSJ, Diagnostician Lachlichi, said that it, too, had similar reservations about the Melfans and Tralthans who were appearing in increasing numbers in the chlorine-breathing levels. It said that in the interests of saving time, O'Mara's answer might be modified to answer both questioners.

"A correct assumption, Lachlichi," O'Mara said. "Both questions have the same general answer." He waited until there was silence before going on. "Many years ago my department initiated a plan which called for the widest possible other-species experience being made available to those staff members with what I judged to be the required degree of psychological adaptability and professional aptitude. Rather than specializing in the treatment of patients belonging to their own or a similar physiological classification, these people were assigned an often-bewildering variety of cases and given responsibility for them which was not always commensurate with their rank at the time. The success of the plan can be measured by the fact that two of the original selectees are at this meeting"—he glanced at Conway and at someone else who was concealed by the intervening bulk of Semlic's life-support system—"and the others are coming along nicely. The degree of success achieved warranted the enlargement of the original project without, however, lowering the original high requirements."

"I had no knowledge of this," Lachlichi said, its spiny, membranous body stirring restively inside its envelope of yellow fog. Ergandhir clicked its lower mandible and added, "Nor I, although I suspected that something like this might be going on."

Both Diagnosticians were staring toward the head of the table, at Thornnastor.

"It is difficult to keep secrets in this place," the Senior Diagnostician said, "and particularly for me. The requirements are a much greater than average ability to understand, generally get along with, actually like, and instinctively do the right thing where a large number of different intelligent species are concerned. But it was decided that neither the entities selected nor their colleagues and immediate superiors should be made aware of the plan lest candidates displaying many of the required qualities fall short of reaching the top and end up as respected and professionally gifted Senior Physicians. In many cases, these entities are capable of better work than their, at times, multiply absentminded superiors; they have no reason to feel ashamed or dissatisfied . . ."

I've flunked it, Conway thought bitterly, *and Thorny is trying to tell me as gently as possible.*

". . . And in any case," Thornnastor went on, "there is a fair chance that they will make it in time. For this reason the existence of the Chief Psychologist's plan and selection procedure must not, for obvious reasons, be discussed with anyone other than those here present."

Maybe there was still a chance for him, Conway thought, especially as he was being told of O'Mara's plan. But another part of his mind was still trying to accept the strange idea of a close-mouthed and secretive Thornnastor instead of the being who was reputed to be the worst gossip in the hospital, when O'Mara resumed speaking.

"It is not the intention," the Chief Psychologist said, "to promote people beyond the level of their professional competence. But the demands on this hospital make it necessary for us to put the medical and"—he glanced at Colonel Skempton—"maintenance resources to the fullest possible use. Regarding the Nallajim invasion of the Chalder wards, I have found that if a doctor or nurse is in more danger from the patient than the patient is from the disease or, as will be the case in the chlorine wards, the patient is in greater danger from the sheer physical mass of its medical attendants than its disease, a great deal of extra care is exercised all around and there is a beneficial effect on the doctor-patient relationship.

"And while we are on the subject of the plan," O'Mara went on, "I have a short list of names which, in my opinion, and subject to your judgment on their professional competence, merit a rise in status to Senior Physician. They are Doctors Seldal, Westimorral, Shu, and Tregmar. A Senior Physician who should be considered for elevation to Diagnostician is, of course, Prilicla... Your mouth is open, Conway. Do you have a comment?"

Conway shook his head, then stammered, "I... I was surprised that a Cinrusskin would be seriously considered. It is fragile, overly timid, and the mental confusion caused by the multiple personalities would endanger it further. But as a friend I would be biased in its favor and would not want to—"

"There is no entity on the hospital staff," Thornnastor said ponderously, "who would not be biased in favor of Prilicla."

O'Mara was staring at him with eyes, Conway knew, which opened into a mind so keenly analytical that together they gave the Chief Psychologist what amounted to a telepathic faculty. Conway was glad that his empath friend was not present, because his thoughts and feelings were nothing to be proud of—a mixture of hurt pride and jealousy. It was not that he was envious of Prilicla or that he wished to belittle the empath in any way. He was honestly delighted that its future prospects were so good. But to think of it being groomed for a position among the hospital's elite while he might well remain just an able and respected Senior Physician!...

"Conway," O'Mara said quietly, "suppose you tell me why Prilicla is being considered for Diagnostician status. Be as biased or unbiased as you like."

For a few seconds Conway was silent as he strove for objectivity in the minds of his alter egos as well as his own—when he was thinking petty thoughts his mind partners kept bringing forward their equivalents. Finally, he said, "The added danger of physical injury might not be as great, since Prilicla has spent its whole lifetime in avoiding physical and psychological damage, and this situation would continue even if it was confused initially by a number of mind-partners. The confusion might not be as bad as I had first assumed, because, as an empath, it is already familiar with the feelings of a very wide range of physiological types, and it is the presence of these alien thoughts and feelings which causes most of the mental confusion in us nonempaths.

"During many years' close professional association with this entity," Conway went on, "I have observed its special talents in use and have noted that it has assumed increased responsibilities which have, on many occasions, involved it in severe emotional discomfort. The most recent incidents were its organizing and direction of the Menelden rescue and its invaluable assistance during the delivery of the Unborn. When the Gogleskan Khone arrives I can think of nobody better able to reassure and..."

He broke off, aware that he was beginning to wander off the subject, and ended simply, "I think Prilicla will make a fine Diagnostician."

Silently, he added, *I wish someone were here saying nice things about me.*

The Chief Psychologist gave him a long, searching look,

then said drily, "I'm glad we agree, Conway. That little empath can obtain maximum effort from both its subordinates and superiors, and without being the slightest bit obnoxious about it the way some of us are forced to be." He smiled sourly and went on. "However, Prilicla will need more time, another year at least in charge of the medical team on *Rhabwar*, and additional responsibilities on the wards between ambulance calls."

Conway was silent, and O'Mara went on. "When your FOKT friend is admitted to the hospital and I have it available for the full spectrum of psych tests, I'm pretty sure that I will be able to eradicate its mind impression, and the one you left in its mind. I won't go into the details now, but you won't be burdened with that troublesome Gogleskan material for much longer."

O'Mara stared at him, obviously expecting a word of thanks, or some kind of response, but Conway could not speak. He was thinking about the lonely, long-suffering, nightmare-ridden, and yet not entirely unhappy individual who shared his thoughts and influenced his actions, so subtly on occasions that he was scarcely aware of it, and of how uncomplicated life would be if his mind were completely his own again—except, that was, for the taped entities, who could be erased at any time. He thought of the presence of Khone, who got the twitches every time a non-Gogleskan life-form went past, which was very often at Sector General, and of the implication its visit had toward the finding of a solution to its species-wide psychosis. But mostly he thought of its unique ability to withdraw and compartmentalize its thinking and its perpetually curious and careful viewpoint which made Conway want to double-check everything he thought and did and which would no longer be there to slow him down. He sighed.

"No," he said firmly, "I want to keep it."

There were a number of untranslatable sounds from around the table while O'Mara continued to watch him unblinkingly. It was Colonel Skempton who broke the silence.

"About this Gogleskan," he said briskly. "What particular problems will it give my department? After the

Protector and Junior's Rumpus Room and the sudden demand for Hudlar prosthetic limbs—"

"There are no special requirements, Colonel," Conway broke in, smiling, "other than a small isolation compartment with a restricted visitors list and normal environment for a warm-blooded oxygen-breather."

"Thank Heaven for that," Skempton said with feeling.

"Regarding the Hudlar prosthetics," Thornnastor said, turning an eye toward the Colonel. "There will be an additional requirement there due to the pregeriatric amputation procedure suggested by Conway, which has since received the approval of the Chief Psychologist and, apparently, every aging FROB that O'Mara has approached. There are going to be far too many voluntary amputees for the hospital to accommodate, so your department will not be involved in the large-scale manufacture of Hudlar prosthetics, but . . ."

"I'm even more relieved," the Colonel said.

". . . We will have our designs mass-produced on Hudlar itself," Thornnastor went on. "The operations will be performed there as well, by Hudlar medics who will be trained at this hospital in the necessary surgical techniques. This will take time to organize, Conway, but I am making it your responsibility, and I would like you to give it a high degree of priority."

Conway was thinking of their one and only Hudlar medic under training, and the large numbers of same-species trainees who would be joining it, and wondering if their personalities and dispositions would be as attractive and friendly. But then he thought of the living hell the patients in Hudlar Geriatric were going through, with the fully functioning brains trapped inside their disease-ridden, degenerating, and pain-racked bodies, and he decided that the training program would be given a high degree of priority indeed.

"Yes, of course," he said to Thornnastor. To O'Mara he added, "Thank you."

Thornnastor's eyes curled disconcertingly to regard everyone at the same time, and it said, "Let us conclude this meeting as soon as possible so that we can get back to running the hospital instead of talking interminably about it. O'Mara, you have something to say?"

"Only the completion of my suggested list of promotions and appointments," the Chief Psychologist said. "I'll be brief. One name, Conway, subject to satisfactory completion of the verbal examination by those present, to be confirmed in his present status and appointed to the position of Diagnostician-in-Charge of Surgery."

Thornnastor's eyes waved briefly along the table before returning to O'Mara. It said, "Not necessary. No dissent. Confirmed."

When the congratulations were over, Conway sat staring at the Chief Psychologist while their more massive colleagues cleared the exit, thinking that he would feel very pleased with himself when the shock wore off. O'Mara was staring back at him, his expression as grim and sour-faced as ever, but with a look in his eyes which was very much like paternal pride.

"The way you've been hacking through patients these past few weeks," O'Mara said gruffly, "what else did you expect?"

About the Author

JAMES WHITE was born in Belfast, Northern Ireland, and resides there, though he spent his early years in Canada. His first story was printed in 1953. He has since published well-received short stories, novellas, and novels, but he is best known for the Sector General series, which deals with the difficulties involved in running a hospital that caters to many radically different life-forms.